1959

UNCONQUERABLES

I consider Mr. Paučo's book *Unconquerables* a milestone in the world's battle against godless Communism, comparable to *Uncle Tom's Cabin* in our own national struggle against slavery. For *Uncle Tom's Cabin* was an intensely human-interest story which aroused the North against the enslavement of the colored people. *Unconquerables* is also an absorbing story, capable of arousing decent men against enslavement by godless Communism.

ANDREW BACHLEDA

UNCONQUERABLES

By JOSEPH PAUCO

Translated from the Slovak by

ANDREW BACHLEDA

VANTAGE PRESS

NEW YORK   WASHINGTON   CHICAGO   HOLLYWOOD

FIRST EDITION

Copyright, 1958, by Joseph Paučo

Published by Vantage Press, Inc.
120 West 31st Street, New York 1, N. Y.

To

REVEREND JOHN J. LACH

Patron of Slovak Literature in the Free World.

FOR reasons of personal security, it has been necessary to present some of the characters under fictitious names. The basic structure of the work, however, is factual; only several minor details are imaginary.

Introduction

THE AFTERMATH of World War II found me
a witness of the horrors of Communism in Slovakia. I lived
through oppression and studied at close range the tactics of
the secret police. I observed the persecution of the faithful,
of bishops, priests, and men and women consecrated by
religious vows. By the hand of God I was made His instru-
ment in a free world, for it is only by the dispensations of
Divine Providence that I was enabled to escape the snares
of Communist guards and secret agents at the borders.

In my book *The Deliverance of Sister Cecilia,* I described
what I myself had endured and witnessed. In this book of
Joseph Paučo, *Unconquerables,* new light has been thrown
upon the current state of affairs in Slovakia. *Unconquerables*
will inform the free world of the tragic fate of the church,
as well as of organized groups, religious communities and of
many individuals. Although many characters appear under
fictionalized names, I can recognize them readily, and would
be able to identify them.

Using data supplied by Slovak escapees, Doctor Paučo
has written a book which illuminates the cruel problems
facing the Slovak nation. It is but natural that men dedicated
to literature are bound to inform the free Western world
of the agonies, the aspirations, and the just merits of the
Slovak nation. To the Slovaks also is due a full measure of
freedom; and it is only in an independent republic that they
will be able to enjoy also the consolations of religion.

Unconquerables contains chapters which may seem incredible, judged by the standards of individuals who have been spared communist domination; however, as a witness of the evolution of Communism in Slovakia after 1945, I vouch that such incidents as Doctor Paučo describes in his book did really occur. In fact, even more terrible events still remain to be exposed to a free world.

Unconquerables has been written with love for the Slovak nation, and I believe that the reader will accept it in the same spirit.

SISTER M. CECILIA

A Spider on the Horizon

A MODEST Bavarian frontier home quartered five Slovak refugees. These men were isolated in a totally strange world. Although cut off from home and country, they hoped to reach the protection of the friendly West. But thus far nothing had happened.

Their long talks concerning the miserable situation of their native Slovakia were interrupted only by the occasional appearance of their landlady, asking for the rent and a little pittance in addition. For such was the custom with both Austrians and Germans: they would ask refugees for cigarettes, chocolates for kiddies, or for any kind of confection. Germans were hungry, for the War had ruined them.

This Bavarian lady also asked the Slovak refugees for something to give her poor little triplets.

A Slovak is ever ready to share even his last crumb of bread with others. He likes to share—both his joys and sorrows. His sensitive nature makes it pleasant for him to lighten the burdens of his fellow man, and he is ever willing to lend a helping hand. That is why this people has emerged victorious from even the greatest of trials.

But it doesn't pay to be too generous in exile. Among strangers one never knows when spiders will cast their deadly nets over you. Unnoticed spiders, oftentimes people with spider-like tendencies, kill their victims in snares skillfully designed to entrap the poor refugee.

11

"We should be more circumspect in speech and should not give away everything," said Pavol.

But he struck a discordant note with his four over-enthusiastic companions. They thought Pavol was timid and wanted to hang on to the meager supply of provisions given them by an American soldier of Slovak descent after they had acquainted him with their tale of woe in exile.

Andrej, his partner in adversity, corrected Pavol, saying, "We must live with people as decency demands."

"Right. But we ourselves are in want; and it is my nature not to trust everyone I hear, no matter how smooth his tongue. Why, even our very own countrymen are capable of harming us! You know it as well as I do that some of them at home rave daily not only against capitalists, but even against us, defenseless refugees. They send out their agents to track us down, with tragical results for all whom they ensnare."

"You are rather timid," Julius responded. "Be courageous! Not every corner hides an agent."

"Would that you were right—but we should be more prudent."

"There's always a happy medium between two extremes," chimed in Ludo. "Pavol is right to warn us to be considerate of our own welfare and not to trust everyone we meet; Andrej is also right in saying that we are not being tracked down. After all, we are but ordinary escapees, just a few individuals among the many millions in Germany today. They certainly would be foolish to waste their time on nondescripts of our type."

Pavol, however, clung to his ideas, and the rest kidded him about them. One would say that he had just seen an agent; another that a stranger asked about Pavol.

Pavol did not heed the saying, "He who laughs last, laughs best." Neither did he associate with people much nor waste provisions.

Once Andrej met a young fellow who was tall, green-eyed, and always carried a cane and a book. The volume was much too large to be a notebook, and Pavol wondered why

12

a refugee would be carrying around so large a tome.

This young fellow's name was Cyril, and he presented himself as a refugee. His clothing indicated that he might be one. He related in detail his escape from Bratislava: but many others had told like tales, so this did not make him conspicuous. He talked a lot, as though he were a typical son of Slovak parentage. Since he was young—if he really were an escapee—he too missed his home and wanted to make up for it by his new association. After all, every one of them was young and inexperienced in worldly ways.

But Pavol was suspicious, kept his distance from Cyril, and spoke little to him, answering his questions curtly.

Andrej was the first to notice this; and it may have irritated him that Pavol avoided the man, for it was Andrej who had introduced Cyril and divided his provisions with him, even giving him a shirt.

"You shouldn't be that way, Pavol."

"What do you mean? Am I supposed to fall into his arms? You may play with fire if you wish, but I don't trust him. I don't like his looks; he talks too much. Juro and yourself are so interested in him that you fail to notice that he is but a fox, trying to pump you for all he can get out of you."

"Aw, go on! You see ghosts even outside of closets."

"Have your fun. But if you stop to consider, you will notice that Cyril seeks to learn where the greater groups of escapees are located, who their leader is, who supports us, what ties we have with Americans and the British, and if there are military, political or any other kinds of connections."

"True, he has asked those questions; but wouldn't you have done likewise? Every one of us is concerned about having a reliable leader on whom we may depend, and that we should have good connections with Western powers. After all, that's why we left Slovakia."

"Yes, I too would have sought such information; but my attitude would have been different. Notice his accent and commentary on everything. He always has something to suggest and fill in, in order to induce us to divulge more and

13

more. I seek not to do him injustice, but I fear that everyone who confides in him blindly will pay for it in the end."

"You are wrong, Pavol."

"You should say—*would* that you were wrong!"

"Have it your way; I trust Cyril. See what happens."

"But that doesn't mean that you have to be foolish about it."

So Andrej became Cyril's friend. Once they paid the UNRRA camp a visit to see if by chance they could find any Slovaks there. They found but two Ukrainians, men who had lived in Slovakia when it had been a republic. But they would not talk much with the young Slovaks.

"They seemed to be secluded and rather self-centered," said Andrej. "Outside of the fact that they praised President Tiso and his very considerate administration in the Republic of Slovakia, they would say nothing."

"Every prudent person in a strange country does likewise," answered Pavol with satisfaction.

For several weeks the life of the five refugees and their new partner, Cyril, remained unchanged. As the season became warmer, they spent more time outdoors. In one thing they accepted Pavol's advice—to walk in pairs, or in threes at the most.

One evening Cyril and Andrej came home late. Andrej confided to Juro that they had decided to cross over "to the other side."

"Where to—Austria or Slovakia?"

"First we'll go over to Austria, where Cyril can size up the situation. If conditions are good, we'll go on to Slovakia. He knows his way around and has friends on the other side of the Danube. He leaves for Austria tomorrow. If he does not return in two days, I'll follow. But don't tell anyone anything about this."

Juro promised, but was sorry for it later.

Cyril left, and two days later Andrej was also gone.

Andrej knew his way to Austria, but Cyril had marked out for him new and shorter routes. So Andrej, a devout lad, set out in God's name. His knapsack contained a sweater, a shirt and a prayer book. In order not to reach the first danger point too early, he hid in some bushes and recited the Litany of the Blessed Virgin. Then he surveyed the situation and finally set out.

As he traveled along silently, there was nothing in Nature to disturb him. Nature is most enchanting at dusk. She changes to clean clothing then, as it were; it seems that the atmosphere is being purified at this time, and along with the stars new wanderers take the place of the tired humanity that withdraws to rest and repose.

But there are people who are active even at nighttime. Some have work to do; others hang around, curious about the mysteries of the dark.

Youthful blood is sensual. Even a refugee is curious about what goes on at night. Thus we have Andrej, a young lad, allowing Cyril to persuade him to travel beyond the border after dark. He was without a passport or document of any kind. If anyone, an official guard, for example, had happened to stop him, he wouldn't have been able to prove who he was. He had no papers of any kind, for he had left everything behind with his four fellow refugees in Bavaria.

Cyril had instructed him to do so.

"Your proficiency in German will suffice. If anyone asks you for certification, tell him you have nothing, or that you forgot your papers and left them at home. That will be the best excuse."

Andrej trusted him, for he himself had once gotten rid of all his Slovak credentials. This had happened shortly after the war, when it seemed to him best to start off an entirely new personality. Not that he was ashamed of his Slovak origin, but everyone seemed to grumble against it. A German could not understand Slovak, and all others seemed to view Slovak refugees in a queer fashion, not even calling them by their proper names.

"I am what I am," thought Andrej as he started tearing up his Slovak credentials. It hurt him deeply every time he would throw a fragment of the papers into the brook beside the path. It had seemed to him that the rivulet carried away a part of his life along with the fragments. But he could not afford to waste time on irritated national feelings. The important factor had been to establish himself. Since he had changed countries, he had to change everything from the ground up. Such had been the evolution of Andrej's youthful eccentricity. A swarm of emotions had taken control of his hands, removing the documents from his pockets and tearing them up!

Andrej thought over that past experience as the view of Austrian frontiers dimmed in the distance, for it was growing dusk. "I was a visionary that time," he said to himself. "But what now?" he queried.

He had no time to consider, for he saw an American jeep but a short distance ahead of him. Such regulation army jeeps had been clinking over Austrian and German roads since the war's ending. Normally, this was nothing to be alarmed about; but at such a time and place, for a person who had set out on a forbidden journey, it was a precarious situation.

Andrej was shaken. Perhaps soldiers were guarding the road to the other side. What was he to do, turn back? That would be a foolish move. Better to go right ahead as though he took notice of nothing going on.

With this thought in mind, he set out. He tried to make it as noiselessly as possible, but kept right on. As he passed the jeep, he noticed it was enclosed. He passed safely by, without a challenge.

But Andrej kept looking back to see if anyone had followed him. He would walk a distance, then stop to listen whether he could hear any footsteps or conversation. But all remained quiet. The sky thickened with stars and an owl hooted from a nearby grove.

Andrej now became more alert. After every ten or fifteen steps he would look ahead sharply to see if anyone was coming over against him, or whether he might see anything suspicious on either side of the road.

"Who knows whether it wouldn't have been safer to travel by pathway, instead of on the open highway?" he asked himself. But Cyril had advised him to travel on the open road, in order to arouse the least suspicion. And he could be right.

There wasn't much time left for meditation. At a distance of about a stone's throw was the River Inn. It seemed to be rather wide. The bridge itself could be a half-mile long. Andrej would go a little farther, in order not to be too far up and thus hit the town on the other side, where he had been directed to a certain address.

Now he became even more circumspect in order to observe anyone who might unexpectedly stop his progress. First he went down to the water's edge; then he made ready the rubber boat Cyril had given him—with a warning not to pump it up too hard, for fear it would blow out. Then he tried rowing it carefully with his hands. "Don't splash, for you know not where a guard might be stationed!" he had been warned.

Andrej strived to obey Cyril's orders, but somehow his hands trembled. "And I am even supposed to shed my clothing, so as to be better able to swim if something should happen! Brrr! . . ." It wasn't easy, but he persuaded himself to do so. For it certainly would be ridiculous for a 23-year-old to be afraid to risk the water, he thought to himself.

Finally, overcoming his reluctance, he was ready to go. He placed the boat at the river's edge; then, bundling his clothing into his knapsack and slinging it over his left shoulder, he held the boat with his right hand till he reached deeper water. When the water was already belt-deep, he placed the knapsack into the boat and, blessing himself, eased into it himself.

"In God's name, forward, Andrej!"

"Is it really in God's name, or is it in Cyril's?" protested the voice of his conscience. But Andrej soon forgot the quotation, for he had to row.

He endeavored to row crosswise, in order not to be too close to the bridge. At first his progress was smooth, and he was confident. But in a short time the current seemed to be working against him. This is but imagination, Andrej. Courage! He paddled on. But just as he thought he had

everything under control, he seemed to hear breathing—
then hissing.

The boat gave way. Something was wrong. Either the boa
was torn or the valve loosened. Before he could realize wha
actually happened, he slid down on the knapsack and fel
water underneath. It was cool water, for at the Austria
frontiers it is still cool around the last of May, especially a
night.

Andrej got an involuntary cold bath. He needed all hi
energy and swimming skill to make it, for a strong Andre
would never give up hope. He skillfully set his hands an
feet in motion and tried swimming the river. But the farthe
he swam, the more his hope faded, for he was approximatel
in the center of the river. The current seemed to be stron
and one of his shoulders was growing weaker.

He made another effort. Extending his strength, h
stretched out both shoulders. He seemed to be progressin
But this was only imagination, for the current was bearin
him down towards the bridge. He lifted up his head an
looked up at the bridge. It wasn't far away, and much clos
than either bank of the river.

But what now? Will he come directly under the bridge,
will he be drawn past it? When he glanced over the fu
length of the bridge, he noticed lights on both ends. Mo
probably a Bavarian guard on the one end, and an Austria
sentry on the other.

There was no further guessing. Despair was close at han
But Andrej did not give up.

"May God's will be done," he said to himself as he allowe
the current to carry him on. He turned over on his back
rest a little. He began to freeze . . . and that he feared th
most. Not that he was sensitive, but cold water will weak
even strong nerves and healthy lungs.

He was but a few feet away from the bridge now. He n
ticed that he was floating directly towards a post, and th
was his salvation. It was a strong concrete pillar, appro
mately in the center of the river. What a support! And
hugged the pillar as though he had fallen into the arms

his own mother . . . or of the Catherine he had left so sorrowfully behind in Slovakia.

He caught hold of the pillar in order to keep his greatest enemy, the wild current, from dragging him any farther. The pillar was rather thick, but just above the water line was an ascent on which Andrej could even sit. He took off his shorts, wrung them out, and wiped the cool beads off his body. He tried everything he could to restore his circulation.

But he couldn't afford to stay there long; he had to move on. He felt the girth of the pillar and, stretching his arms, encircled it. This enabled him to climb higher. Now a sweat dripped from his brow. He was afraid of this, for a fever might overtake him. He felt the pillar again, but could find nothing else to reach. He tried the other side, and there he found something like a small stone sticking out of the concrete. This helped him to get up four feet higher. He had now but a short distance to go to reach the bridge itself. However, this was the bottom side of the bridge, and at the river's center. At that moment he seemed to hear footsteps. He listened. Yes, it was the sound of heavy footsteps on the bridge! Surely, the sentry! Andrej shrank involuntarily and held his breath.

As luck would have it, the sentry did not come all the way over to the center of the bridge. The man returned, and Andrej breathed a sigh of relief as he started feeling again, first with the right, then with the left hand. Finally, he reached the bridge itself. A beam projected outward so that he could feel it, but this was still not enough. He started sweating again and felt himself growing weaker. He was hungry and his eyes were closing for lack of sleep.

But he must hold out. Surely, he would find a way to save himself! He felt again, and this time found a strong nail on the Austrian side of the beam. He was saved! He tried the nail with his right hand while clinging to the beam with his left. This helped, and he hung on to the nail.

Now to make further progress. He drew himself entirely under the bridge, and into a contracted position. Then he caught hold of a strong nail with his left and reached out

19

for another beam with his right. He found it—and also another nail—so he hung on and supported his feet against the first beam. When he had a good grip on the nail, he slowly let go of the beam with his feet and extended his body over the water. Only his strong right arm saved him from falling.

He tried the same thing again a second and a third time, and reached another pillar. Feeling his way to the landing, he rested. He also saw light—this time from the Austrian city. This gave him added strength and hope. Blessing himself, he again sought another beam. He found it, and hoped to be on the other side of the bridge soon.

But this hope was short-lived, for he was not destined to get by under the bridge that easy, even though he had beams, nails and steps to go by, and Andrej still thought himself strong enough to do so. For this was not wrestling with other youngsters on a pasture field—wood was much more treacherous. Moreover, water had penetrated deeply under his hide. Andrej began to tremble. The more he rested on beams, the more he weakened. Yet he dared to reach out for another beam; but this was a dangerous attempt. His right arm did not reach a nail, and his left had become so weakened that he lost his hold on the beam and fell into the water.

He made a loud splash as he took a cold bath for the second time that night. But this turned out to be advantageous for Andrej, as the water refreshed him, he later realized. . . . But not till three days later, when he recalled the adventure.

The water was cold; but he had no time to think about that now as he desperately sought a pillar. He had fallen between two of them; surely, he could reach one. He succeeded, but not till he was practically exhausted. Grabbing hold of the pillar, he tried to pull himself up out of the water.

But just at that moment he heard footsteps and a voice: "Something splashed into the river, and it must have been rather heavy, for I distinctly heard it on the other side," said a man in German.

"Maybe it was but your imagination," answered the other sentry. "Why would people want to splash about in water at this time of the night?" The men passed above Andrej and went on to the center of the bridge, then returned. He scarcely dared to breathe, but this helped him.

He trembled with cold, but was determined not to call for help. A pride was awakened in him, and maybe he was already in a delirium of fever. But he did not give up.

In a little while he resumed his "journey" under the bridge. He took more rest at every beam, and this helped him out. When he neared the end of the bridge, he again listened for footsteps or voices. Everything was quiet, for it was already past midnight; and the guards too, probably, wanted to rest their eyelids a little.

At the last pillar he already dropped to solid ground. It was damp shore, but not as cold as water, and he felt better. Now he dragged himself along the shore on hands and knees in order to get as far away as possible from the bridge.

He succeeded. Now he strained his ears to make sure everything was safe. Not a bird, not even a butterfly, fluttered. This was fortunate for secret and illegal traveling. It was also good for you, naked Andrej!

Thus far, he remained unconscious of the fact that he was naked, except for shorts. Now he became aware of it. He sat down on the shore, bent himself all the way over, and stretched out, doing all the setting-up exercises he had learned as an Eagle Scout. He exercised tirelessly, in order to restore his circulation and banish from his mind the recent danger. When his circulation again became normal, he breathed a heartfelt sigh of thanksgiving to God that he was still alive.

"If Cyril spoke the truth, they will save me," he thought.

This was the first time he had said to himself: "*If* Cyril spoke the truth."

Why? Because he could have gone to Austria by another route. He knew his way; but Cyril had coaxed him to come this way, saying that he had "connections" only here.

Andrej stretched out and immediately lay down again. Then he crawled up to the top of the embankment to see more. After every movement he stopped to listen. He was very careful lest he fall into unwelcome arms now.

He crawled over the bank; and when the bridge had already become dim to his view, he ventured to stand up on his feet. He stepped out on clean, dry earth. He found himself in a field adjacent to the river. He was not far from the town which was to shelter him, where he could get hot tea and clothing.

He looked around and started to walk. "I must reach a dry warm place as soon as possible, to avoid serious illness. At least shelter—at the quickest."

He remembered the street and exact address, as Cyril had given it to him. He also remembered the kind of house he should enter. He would go through the garden and rap on the third window.

He did so, and a voice responded, *"Wer ist da?"*

It struck Andrej strangely that Germans had answered. According to Cyril, Slovaks were to have answered.

"Does a Slovak refugee named Krošliak live here?"

"Was wollen Sie?"

At this Andrej asked in Slovak: "Are you Slovaks?"

He received no answer, but two men appeared at the window and asked for the prearranged password.

"Beskýdy Mountains covered with snow," responded Andrej.

"Enter through the door at the right. They have been open for you for the past hour."

The spider had crawled after Andrej, but did not get him. He wanted to kill him in the River Inn, but he had escaped. "Thank God! At last I am sheltered and among Slovaks. I trust Cyril." That thought accompanied him into the vestibule of the home.

Captive

ANDREJ HAD reached shelter and was among friends. Slovaks had welcomed him, giving him a comfortable bed. And he did go to bed at once, for there was no

22

much use talking in the dead of night and he was utterly exhausted.

Next morning it was hard for him to get up. His fevered eyes made for a heavy head. Andrej broke out into a heavy sweat and came down with a fever. The two new friends who took care of him were not as sincere as those he had left behind in the Bavarian lodging, and they were getting a little nervous.

"We can't afford to get you a doctor, for you are penniless, and we are as poor as you are. Moreover, sickness will break up our schedule."

"How much time have we?" asked Andrej.

"But three days. Within that time you must be in Vienna, where Cyril is waiting for you."

"Let's hope I can make it."

Andrej had no alternative. He had to consider himself and his health, in order not to disappoint Cyril. Otherwise, he couldn't be trusted.

The fever let up, and Andrej could talk a little, but there was little to say.

"You will board the train this evening," said the dark-complexioned 40-year-old Slovak.

He issued this order in the tone of a father ordering his son firmly.

"I understand that," answered Andrej. "But where will I get clothing and certification? I am aware of the fact that one must have personal permission to travel in Vienna. Moreover, I am afraid to cross the Red Zone."

"Fear not, friend, everything is in order," added the younger attendant. "Cyril and his friends left everything you will need to get safely to Vienna. Once there, Cyril himself will look after you. I know he will take good care of you."

This seemed to quiet Andrej's fears. His companions stressed every word with its natural accent. It was hard to doubt them. Neither did Andrej *intend* to doubt, for he was delighted by the idea of new adventures, pleasures and good times. He would probably go to Bratislava, and maybe to his home town. How this would be accomplished did not worry him, for he trusted Cyril. The promise of new exploits and a new home made Andrej a daring young man.

He drank some hot tea and covered himself with a blanket, in order to regain his strength more readily. His appetite returned and he ate a good meal. For one must eat to be strong enough for adventure. Otherwise, struggle, journey and plans are useless. Everything requires physical and mental strength.

Andrej decided to try out his legs. That afternoon he got up for some fresh air and in order to strengthen his leg muscles. He had a great mission to accomplish.

But he stumbled. His head was again as heavy as a bell—puffed up and heavy, like a cast-iron bell. But he did not give up. He did not return to bed, but kept fighting his weakness, and his companions encouraged him in the struggle. They knew it to be their duty, for Cyril had given them orders; and either this evening or tomorrow they were to get new charges. They said they were waiting for refugees from the French occupation zone of Austria who had arrived from Tyrol. "We have 'our people' living there also," explained the dark-complexioned elder friend.

Andrej did not feel at his best, but he would not show this in his bearing. Gritting his teeth, he forced himself to walk. When he got tired, he would sit down for a while. As his aches eased up, he regained his composure and asked for clothing.

"For the present, wear what I gave you. Before the train leaves, I will get you respectable clothing that Cyril left for you."

"Did he leave clothing for me?" he asked himself. "He certainly was kind-hearted and thought of everything. He probably foresaw that I could easily lose my only clothing. Or? Or? . . . But banish the thought! No 'or' about it. Cyril took good care of me, and thought of every possibility. I must be grateful for that. I must also be grateful to the men here, for they are also our native Slovak brethren in exile. Here they eat hard black bread and live in a small roomlet, even as we have been living in Bavaria, and thousands of others are so existing. They live but to maintain life, and to care for others, in addition. True Samaritans, good people, sincere Slovaks! Today we need such manhood. For degraded men get you nowhere, arouse no one, and inspire no enthusiasm."

Such were Andrej's thoughts when the younger companion aroused him by tapping him on the shoulder and reminding him that he must get ready for the journey. He gave him an old knapsack, rather ragged and quite greasy and dirty.

"This is exactly what you need. Since you are setting out on a rather long journey, you must be all the less conspicuous."

Andrej began to wash himself; but his companion restrained him and instructed him rather to daub himself with a little charcoal here and a little dirt there. For he must pretend to be a hard-working man seeking employment and reunion with his family, willing to take anything he is given along the way, and to do even the hardest kind of work.

They pulled a live fir tree out of the room corner. It looked as though it had been made ready for Christmas, whereas it was but the last of May.

"Seize this tree with both your hands, and try to get as much resin as you can on your hands, palms and all ten fingers. Then, instead of washing them, rather dirty them with more earth. You have thick fingers; this will help you to appear as circumstances require, in view of the journey ahead of you."

Then came the time for him to leave for the station.

"Now you will dress up," the elder man ordered. "Here is the clothing Cyril had left for you, together with the documents. You will be called Johann Kurtschmidt, and you will go to Vienna as a war prisoner. Your home is supposed to be there and your family is waiting for your return. You have a wife and two children. That much for officials, if you should be questioned. But your real destination is that address I am giving you, which you must memorize. There Cyril will be waiting for you an hour before train arrival. You must remember that address; and especially do not forget your name and the idea that you are supposed to be returning from captivity."

25

Then they tried him out. He was asked where he had been captured; then his name; and the third question concerned the address he was to contact. This was repeated several times. Andrej knew all the answers.

The elder man then gave him the clothing, which was a German uniform.

"Am I supposed to go in uniform?"

"How else? You are supposed to be returning from captivity. This is the best scheme anyone could devise. Herr Kurtschmidt, that is the best for you. Get dressed, for the train leaves in half an hour."

"*Your address?*"

"*Name?*"

"*What camp were you captured in?*"

"*What have you been doing till now?*"

Andrej did not even make a break in this examination. His German was fluent and his thoughts flowed steadily, even though his eyes were still bright with fever.

It was getting dark. Andrej—Johann—disappeared in the night. The companions quickly closed the door behind him and watched from the window to see if he was going to the station.

He had no difficulty. Chancing to glance at the waiting-room mirror, he saw in it an entirely new individual. He did not recognize himself.

"That's good. I do look like a genuine prisoner of war; I will go out and not get lost. For a Slovak readily adapts himself to all circumstances."

The train hid Johann—Andrej—within its entrails. It was rather crowded, but decent citizens readily crowded together to make room when they noticed the war prisoner. Andrej sat down quietly and reconsidered all that had happened during the past two days. But he soon roused himself, realizing that it was ill advised to think about what *had* happened. Rather, he must face circumstances as they exist and think of the morrow.

"You are a war prisoner—and a German at that. You wear a German uniform. Therefore, you must speak German as

26

much as possible, in order not to be suspected when directors approach, and also when you have to move about in Vienna."

Andrej quickly impressed himself with the idea that he had changed his name and appearance. A chill ran up and down his spine, but that was nothing. He overcame his last indecision and began conversing with fellow passengers. They liked to answer his questions and listen to Johann's tales of knocking over Russians, fights, bombardment, bayonet charges, hunger, misery, lousy uniforms, wounds, hopelessness, wakeful nights. . . .

Such tales had been heard frequently, but they always found some hearers. For although not everyone had gone off to war, yet every German and Austrian had had someone in this hot hell of hate and murder. The floods of dammed up tears and misery mounted higher than the neighboring hills.

Women sighed and the more tender girls wept over Johann. A number of civilians joined in the conversation. Men from World War I added their case histories to that of Johann's, as if to stress the importance of the one or the other battle, and also to testify, as living witnesses, what misery every war brings about.

War-prisoner Johann passed through the review successfully. His documents were genuine. An American, a Frenchman, an Englishman and a squinting Bolshevik grabbed them in order, turned them over once, and then handed them back to Johann, almost tenderly. The tales continued until Johann became tired and closed his eyes. He wanted to have a little quiet, in order to evaluate what would await him in Vienna. Cyril, new quarters, then what? . . .

Cyril would care for him, even as his friends had done on the frontier. They had nursed him, fed him and given him a drink; outfitted him properly with a uniform; and then made him out to be a war prisoner.

Many of his fellow passengers did not go as far as Vienna; a majority got off before they reached the Soviet occupation zone. One cursed terribly when they would not allow him to visit his sick mother, who was somewhere near the American-Russian frontier but on undivided Austrian territory.

"I have read a lot about them liberating us. And here we have occupation armies on our neck! How long will this last? A year should suffice. Such liberty!"

No one answered him. Some probably did not want to, others agreed with him in spirit. Austrians had plenty to tell, but what good would it have done here on the train? Better to follow prevailing discipline, for one must live and think of the morrow. A man even voiced this aloud; and the train seemed to punctuate his remark when it suddenly jolted the passengers.

At the station in Vienna Andrej had to pass through civil and army inspection, four in uniforms and four in various languages and style of clothing.

The Russian stopped him and vainly spoke in Russian, for Johann did not answer. He explained very little, even to the interpreter. He had been in war, fought, killed as others had done, and now he was here, close to his family. He wanted to go home, and felt lucky that in a while his wife would give him some tea and hug him, and he in turn would press her to his chest and play with his daughters. And best of all, he could forget about the army and commands. This latter remark seemingly irritated a Russian junior officer. Laughing from the side of his mustache, he playfully gave Johann the papers back.

"Everything went along smoothly," thought Andrej to himself as he found himself before the door of a house on a certain street. He knocked on the door. It was already morning, so he would not awaken her from her dreams, for the "wife" would be up by this time.

The door opened. There appeared suddenly the green eyes of Cyril.

"*Grüss Gott!*" Johann greeted him, and Cyril answered the same, extending his hand.

Johann quickly disappeared from the street and found himself in a half-cellar room. "His family" lived here.

When he stepped into the middle of the room, Cyril whispered to him in Slovak: "Make yourself at home. Breakfast will soon be ready. In the meantime, wash yourself, shave

28

and dress up. Your civilian clothes are there. However, you will retain your name while in Vienna."

Andrej sighed and was glad that he was in the company of a friend. Everything had turned out well. He shed his uniform, and no longer had to invent tales of war.

But Johann did not shed himself of obligations. Cyril quickly put him on the spot as soon as they drank the coffee and ate two pieces of bread with margarine. And these obligations came in a way Andrej had not expected.

"I take it for granted that you brought along everything," reminded Cyril while he was still wiping his mouth with a napkin.

"That I did not. I had a great accident, my dear Cyril. I rowed that boat as you instructed, but it must have been damaged. A terrible thing happened, so that I almost lost my life."

"That I don't have to believe."

Andrej was taken aback, but recollected himself.

"I have witnesses."

"So? Did you not travel alone?"

"Well, yes, but our two friends who sent me here will tell you that I came to their home dressed in shorts and chilled to the bone."

"Anyone could say that, and arrange matters to suit the tale. You dipped yourself a little in the river when you were already on the other side, and then arrived at the home in but shorts in order to arouse pity."

"But I was quite sick over the experience!"

"Hypocrisy, falsehood, trickery! I noticed how you were evasive from the very beginning, even in Bavaria."

"But did I not talk the others over so as not to wrong you?"

"Even that may have been refined hypocrisy. We understand such birds well. I clearly instructed you not to leave without a message from Louis. It is expressly for that purpose that we want to go to Slovakia."

"But I *did* get everything, even though not as explicitly as you asked for; but it would have sufficed. For it was a mes-

29

sage to Louis' brother, and he in turn would have sent us further ahead."

"Where then is this message?"

"It went down the river, together with my clothing and everything I had."

"You are cheating! You want to spy on me!"

"I know it's hard to believe. After all, we've been acquainted but a short time. Maybe I did commit an error. I did not wrap up that message in cellophane and place it into my mouth, as you had ordered. That was my fault."

"And a fatal fault!"

Here Cyril began to doubt openly whether Andrej was telling the truth. But finally he relented and added: "No one is perfect. You can still correct your mistake. This evening I will introduce you to my friend Martin. We will talk it over with him, to figure out how we should proceed. Maybe you will return to Bavaria and definitely bring back that message —or you might wait till I return from Bratislava."

"Are you going to Bratislava?"

"I leave tomorrow and will return in a week."

"How about me?"

"What would you want to do? You must first declare yourself, and that will take time. I can't afford to take along inexperienced boys to Bratislava."

Beguiling Vienna

ANDREJ COULD not travel to Bratislava, for Cyril did not want him. He had planned it that way. He knew how to go about it without giving away his intentions to Andrej. He had friends in Vienna who saw to it that Andrej's journey to Slovakia was obstructed. Andrej was so close to Slovak borders, yet unable to cross them.

As evening approached, Cyril and Andrej set out for town. They entered a decent tavern, where there was plenty to eat and drink—at Cyril's expense. Andrej hoped that Cyril had forgotten everything, and that he would be friendly and take him along to Bratislava.

Martin arrived, but not alone. A pleasing young brunette accompanied him. Her eyes sparkled and her cheeks were a glowing red. Her lips made Andrej forget himself as soon as he saw her.

Cyril introduced Andrej to the beautiful and carefree girl Sabina, and to her companion Martin. Both men were over-indulgent to Andrej, a fact he failed to notice. For he was feasting his eyes on the dark curls and enticing lips of the girl.

After supper an orchestra struck up and played so enchantingly that Andrej forgot everything. This music was for him . . . and Sabina. He asked her for a dance, and noticed that she liked to dance with him. She herself suggested that they dance the following dreamy waltz, stating that it was not as pleasant for her to dance with either Cyril or Martin. Andrej was a gentleman who could not refuse a girl, especially one who had made such an impression on him.

He bowed and, in accordance with an old mid-European custom, took up her tiny hand and kissed it. After this number he thanked her for the dance and led her to a table. The orchestra struck up again. Quite unexpectedly, the first violinist came up with a Slovak tune. Now Andrej was in his own element. His youthful blood was filled with new desires. Vienna's waltzes brought Andrej closer to Bratislava, but enticing wine brought him closer to loving Sabina, who did not try to conceal her delight in Andrej's company.

Cyril encouraged Andrej to drink up, but Andrej needed no prodding. When Andrej was already half-giddy with waltzing, Cyril slipped away unnoticed. Andrej did not observe that there were only three of them left at the table till much later.

Finally, the music quieted down, lights were dimmed, and the head waiter approached Martin with the bill; but Andrej raised his right hand, calling for more wine.

The man explained that rules would not permit it, as it was closing time. But this did not quiet Andrej. He was thirsty. He was not sure himself whether it was his taste for wine or his desire to remain in Sabina's presence. But he wanted wine!

Finally, Martin and Sabina succeeded in quieting him down by promising him that they were going to have more wine that very evening. Andrej agreed to go along with his new companions. Where did not concern him. He trusted both, and was also aware of the fact that both were acquainted with Vienna's night life.

And they certainly did know all its mysteries and enchantments. Andrej wanted to sing along the way, and his voice did break out, both in German and in Slovak.

They kept on walking, but Andrej did not care. Neither did his companions. As a matter of fact, they wanted to make the walk longer in order to give the cool night air a chance to refreshen tipsy Andrej, for they were going to an important establishment and did not want him to create a scene there with singing and loud talk. Consequently, Sabina and Martin led Andrej by side streets to make the walk last longer.

Finally, they arrived at an establishment which could have served as an office building as well as a youth center. This, however, did not concern Andrej. Neither was he interested in the two young men sitting on a divan who welcomed the company with glasses in hand. They introduced themselves to Andrej, but he did not understand their names. After looking them over, shaking hands, and patting each on the back, he devoted himself exclusively to Sabina, and she to him.

It was hard to tell how long this youthful company amused itself with wine and recorded music. Andrej danced again; and the more he danced, the more he gazed into Sabina's designing eyes. Between dances she would lean over to him and ask: "Do you like me?"

" 'Like' is not the word for it. I would give up the whole world to have you always." That was Andrej's answer.

She kissed him, and they danced again.

When he continued to gaze into her eyes, and her cheeks burned both with wine and passion, she again asked: "Have you any other loves?"

"I did have, but I have forgotten about them. I *had* to forget, and maybe they no longer care for me."

"That's not enough for me. You must give me a direct answer. Have you or have you not?"

"I have not, because I have found you!"

That seemed to satisfy Sabina, for she nestled closer to Andrej and tangled both her hands in his chestnut hair.

The phonograph stopped playing; and they stood motionless on the floor. Martin broke it up by calling them to the table and pouring out wine for them. They also had cigarettes which were exactly like the American kind. In fact, everything pleased Andrej. This was *his* night. So it seemed to him, so whispered the beautiful Sabina, and so feigned his new companions. It would have been better for him had he paid more attention to what they really wanted from him.

But how could he understand?

The world belonged to him. Wine, Sabina, and charming Vienna fascinated Andrej. It aroused in him a new man. He forgot that he was a refugee who had set out for home. He forgot about Cyril in his enjoyment of the new company. His companions were young and gay.

He answered Sabina's whispers as well as her open questions. He closed his eyes when she had allowed him to kiss her after he had again confessed that she was the only girl in his life.

Sabina had Andrej on a string. She succeeded in her quest, as does every beautiful woman who comes upon a dreamy lad. Her sweet words, fervent eyes, and womanly tenderness were a magnet to Andrej.

After a while, wine and cigarettes caused Andrej to fall asleep in Sabina's arms. She searched through his pockets. She even felt under his shirt as she feverishly sought for something.

"Search him thoroughly!" Martin instructed her.

When Andrej half-opened his eyes, she leaned over and kissed him and patted his cheeks, and he smilingly fell asleep again.

Sabina failed to find what she was looking for. Andrej

33

really had no papers on him, neither money nor any secret tokens. What else could she have wanted? What was Martin so curious about?

They did not reveal it to Andrej that evening. He fell asleep, but slept fitfully. He would turn over and talk in his sleep, but unintelligibly. Sabina vainly sought to get something out of him. It seemed that Andrej would mention names; then he would be afraid; and again a smile would appear on his face. Maybe he was reliving his passage from Germany and his pleasures after a sensual night in Vienna.

Morning found Andrej on the divan. He wanted to get up, but his head spun. Drawn window shades prevented him from seeing what time it was. He did not even look for light, but tried to sleep again and could not. He did not know exactly what had happened to him. Only Sabina remained in his imagination, for it was the brightest picture he had seen in a long time. Sabina had danced, Sabina had kissed him, Sabina had patted his cheeks. . . . But what next? Everything was quiet.

Andrej waited for a while. When sleep would not return, he got up and started looking for the bathroom. He washed himself in cold water and felt better.

He pulled up a shade to look out into the street. It was a lovely day, and the sun was already high. Andrej must have slept late.

His head was ringing and his forehead seemed ready to fall off.

"I shouldn't have drunk so much and gone so far." He had time to conjecture, ask himself questions, reproach himself, and even to quiet his conscience.

However, he did not want to admit that Cyril might have wanted to harm him.

"By the way, where *is* Cyril?" Andrej asked himself almost aloud.

No one answered. The walls were silent, and no one was in the room but Andrej. Had they abandoned him?

Wait, Andrej, be not disturbed! You had it good last

night, so be patient. You don't know your way about Vienna. Moreover, your head is heavy. Where would you go?

Andrej decided to wait. He found a German newspaper on the night stand. Looking it over, he could find nothing interesting on either the first or the second page. Only on the third page did he find the word, Slovak.

It was hard for him to read, for his mind was not receptive; but he forced himself and read the brief report: *"It is announced from Bratislava that a young Slovak has been caught trying to cross the Danube Bridge to Pretržalka, and thence likely to Austria. This incident has enabled safety authorities to come upon a whole group prepared for escape."*

Andrej wiped his brow, and his head became clearer at once. Just then he happened to notice the date of the newspaper; it was already a month old! This appeared to him to be a warning, for he too wanted to go to Bratislava and return. More than that he could not grasp, for he was still not quite sober.

Someone knocked on the door.

"Herein!" answered Andrej.

Martin entered. He was surprised to find Andrej already up.

"We thought you would sleep longer, for we were all up till five."

"Till five?" exclaimed Andrej.

"You fell asleep a little earlier. But we left soon after when we finished our wine; and Sabina was already tired out."

"Where is Sabina?"

"She went to work. This is a work day, and she must be at the office every day."

"What kind of work does she do?"

"Didn't she tell you?"

"I forgot to ask her."

"She is a secretary in a certain establishment. She has it good. Better than any of us. She speaks German fluently, also other languages, which helps her out. But we must consider other matters now, Andrej. We must work out a program for

35

the day; and you may meet Sabina at night if you wish to."

"I would like to do that, but I must consider my journey."

"We'll see to that. But first we must ascertain conditions and find out whether everything is in order."

"Why, Cyril was supposed to do that! Where *is* Cyril?"

"Plans were changed. Yesterday the way was clear; but last night someone informed him that guards were alerted along the Morava and Danube Rivers, and that they were setting up wire barricades. Cyril followed up this information to investigate everything accurately."

Martin's convincing words satisfied Andrej. He still thought of Sabina, and somehow she meant more to him than the journey to Slovakia. He allowed Martin to persuade him to come along for a walk to view the ruins of Vienna.

"Americans bombarded this. Here American bombs also fell. And look at that church! That also was their work."

"Where did Russian bombs fall?"

"That I do not know and do not ask about. But someone said that the Russian Army was more considerate."

"Her father is considerate! They are devils!" heatedly replied Andrej.

"Take it easy, Andrej! We are coming to the Soviet sector, and one never knows where he may come across a Russian. I'm not praising the Russian Army. I say only what I heard."

But this disturbed Andrej, and he decided not to enter the Russian zone.

"Nothing will happen to you," Martin tried to dissuade him. "You have your certification; you are an Austrian. We will begin to speak German exclusively. That will save us."

"I will not go, Martin."

"Not even for Sabina?"

"Does Sabina work there?"

"Yes."

Andrej remained thoughtful for a while. Then he said resolutely—"I will not go to the Russian zone, even for Sabina." And he said this in German.

"I'm not urging you, but I'm almost certain that nothing will happen. I am well acquainted with all its establishments.

I also know where we may entertain ourselves without being hampered by control authorities. And even if they should contact us, Russians also are decent people. Many a time I have seen Russian soldiers enjoying themselves in Austrian establishments."

"That doesn't interest me at all."

"But Slovakia *does* interest you. Yet it has the same Soviet controls as in the Russian zones of Austria or Germany. And you would go to Slovakia."

"But I have parents, friends and acquaintances there."

"We are your friends also. And Sabina is crazy over you. You should appreciate her more. She sends you a message that it would please her most if you would meet her in her beloved establishment, located in this sector."

"I will not go, Martin."

"Have it as you will. I know that you would be glad to get to Bratislava soon. But will it make any difference when you get there?"

"Not quite so," responded Andrej.

"What's on your program?"

"I want to see our people."

"And who are 'our' people?"

"My family and remaining upright Slovaks. I would like to see how they live, and how Bratislava and Slovakia in general are changed."

"Then you are concerned about changes. But don't you read papers and hear broadcasts? These sources carry sufficient information."

"A person can't find out everything there. What a person sees with his own eyes means more."

Martin observed Andrej quite well. The accent of his words, the motion of his hands and his eyes told him what Andrej really wanted. And his last remark seemed to satisfy him.

Finally, Martin compromised. He promised Andrej that he would persuade Sabina to come to the American zone for supper and entertainment that evening. Andrej thought it over, but came to no definite conclusion.

Even if they should be wicked, and in the service of Communists, they can do me no harm, he thought. In the meantime Martin went across to a store, while Andrej remained in the room he had slept in.

But they *do* have proofs against you, his conscience reminded him. You did not bring Cyril what he wanted, and this angered him. Be careful!

He decided not to drink too much, which would make the entertainment more agreeable.

And so it happened. But even this caused Martin to doubt him, and Sabina to be cooler than on the previous evening. Andrej did not care to drink, even though Martin and Sabina urged him to, giving him his choice.

While Andrej was twirling Sabina around during a fourth waltz, she spoke to him and asked why he had lost yesterday's good humor.

"I did not lose it; but you know as well as I do that a person can't keep on celebrating every day. I'd rather have a good sleep; then I'd feel better tomorrow."

"But I will not be free tomorrow. I have to work—even at night."

"That's too bad."

"I have been looking forward to this evening, Andrej. But you do not love me, although yesterday you professed fervent love."

"I *do* love you, Sabina. But I don't feel as good as I felt yesterday. We should have celebrated less yesterday; then it would have been better today."

Sabina tried to control herself and pretend to go along with his line of thought. Martin did likewise. But it did not escape Andrej that a certain well-dressed man talked with Martin during the dance. When they parted, he watched the dancers from the doorway. His eyes sought Andrej as though he wanted to remember him well.

Andrej purposely committed a dancing error. Sabina noticed it and looked up at Andrej. She tried to fathom his eyes, asking suspiciously: "Why do you stagger about as though you do not belong to this company?"

"Maybe I don't," pouted Andrej.

This caused Sabina to leave Andrej in a huff.

He followed her and tried to explain that he had not meant it that way. But she was offended and did not speak for quite a while. Andrej found another partner, but after the dance returned to Sabina and Martin.

Sabina spoke through her teeth: "I will forgive you this first time. But act like a man, not like a kitten! You just drag about and can't follow any dancing step."

Martin suggested that it would be better to allow Andrej to rest up, for he had slept but little last night, and gone through a hard journey before that, a fact which was known to Sabina and to the companions who had joined them.

This satisfied Andrej. He hoped to get out of this predicament somehow. He went to the washroom, but Martin was behind him. He took his hat from the cloakroom, but Martin was always close to him. He purposely engaged a girl in conversation, but Martin urged him on, ever at his heels. He listened once more to the "Blue Danube Waltz," but Martin pulled him by the cuff, saying that it was time to go.

Andrej could not help himself. Beguiling Vienna called— but where to?

He found out fast.

Before he could reach the tavern door, Sabina joined him, grasping his right hand. She started caressing him as though nothing had happened. She even asked forgiveness. Andrej wanted to step out into the street, but now Martin held him by the left shoulder as a gun flashed in his other hand.

They made but eight steps, and a car door opened. Andrej disappeared into it. Martin shut the door from the outside; and in the car the man who a short time ago had talked with Martin in the tavern overpowered Andrej, gagged and tied him up. Andrej no longer continued his trip to Slovakia, nor even returned to Bavaria. He disappeared in the midst of Vienna.

A Communist Agent

In a dark chamber, somewhere in the suburbs of Vienna, Andrej pondered over what had happened to him. He had lost his freedom. Outsiders had trapped him. And who brought this about?

Cyril!

He couldn't get rid of this thought; and the more he considered it, the more he was forced to admit that he had been betrayed into the hands of these merciless people, who battered a person around three or four times a day, by Cyril and his associates.

They all played the same game. All were in the service of Communism. Not one of them was a decent person. Now even Andrej knew it. He had not known it before. A good lesson. If he could but warn relatives in Bratislava and Bavaria against Cyril! For he was certain that Cyril would not stop with one victim. A Communist agent is dangerous always, everywhere, and for everyone with whom he comes in contact.

And Cyril did go to Bratislava. He could cross over the Danube easily. He had a boat ready for him on the Austrian side of the river, with a man in it. He gave the password, whereupon the man took him straightway to Devín. There guards gave Cyril a salute, which was an indication that he was their man.

Cyril boldly walked the streets of Bratislava and quartered

himself in the Hotel Carlton. They had a room ready for him. That very evening he paid Andrej's old friend a visit, for Andrej had talked to him about this friend. It wasn't hard to find a person in Bratislava, for the police kept a record of all its inhabitants. If an agent had one name, it was easy for him to find other names and addresses. And Cyril did have them.

He went to Ludo's home that evening. He found him there. For in Bratislava every decent person remained indoors, especially at night, rather than roam about looking for trouble. Nothing attracted a person to the streets, for strangers appeared everywhere. The traditional gaiety had disappeared from the streets of Bratislava. People were being arrested day and night, business establishments confiscated, churches and monasteries robbed, and people executed in the municipal courtyard. No one was anxious to hear and see such things on the streets of Bratislava, much less expose himself to the danger of being dragged off to prison—if not to Siberia or a concentration camp.

Hence, caution kept Andrej's friend Ludo home at night. Andrej and Ludo had grown up together, and both had studied at the University of Slovakia. When the war ended, Andrej had departed for the West, but Ludo remained behind to take care of his weak mother.

But he did not help her much. Authorities expelled him from the university, because someone informed them that Ludo had participated in an anticommunist demonstration and had written two articles against Communism.

When he applied for work, he was asked where he had worked before.

"Nowhere," answered Ludo.

"What do you mean by 'nowhere'?"

"I studied."

"Did you finish up?"

"No."

"Poor student?"

"I was expelled."

"Why?"

41

And there it was.

Business establishments under national control—that is, in the hands of a communist government—would of necessity refuse to give him work. Others were afraid.

Hence Ludo and his mother merely existed. There were hundreds and thousands of others in similar circumstances. Only truly charitable people would help them to ward off hunger and obtain clothing and shoes. Slovakia was changing beyond recognition. There was a shortage of food and work. Only prisons were full; and the concentration camps gave off a mournful dirge. Excessive punishments marked a new era in the history of a people who had not known such misery and oppression in fifteen hundred years.

Ludo was a part of this afflicted people; but he had not yet lived long enough to understand it all. Aided by a monastery, he existed in seclusion. This monastery also cared for his mother. He would go to meet her there and pray with her, and she would give him her blessing to help him bear his hard life better.

As a man of good conscience, he opened the door at Cyril's first knock. He could not see his green eyes and surly expression in the dim light of the evening. Greeting him, he gave him a chair in the center of his humble room.

"I came from Bavaria, and am a refugee. Sometime ago I met your friend Andrej, and I bring you a message from him."

"Where is Andrej? When were you with him?"

"He is safe, and I talked to him two days ago. Since I had a good journey, I reached Bratislava quicker than I thought. Andrej feels fine—much better than you do, I'd venture to say. Americans feed us, help us in every way, and promise even more."

"Thank God!" responded Ludo. "I thank you for the pleasant news. I sure would like to be in your company myself."

"You *can* be."

"I cannot."

"Have you important work to do here?"

"I have to look after my sick mother."

"That can be taken care of. We can arrange it so that you may take care of your mother and be one of us at the same time."

"It would be hard for me to go to Bavaria and leave her here."

"But we *need* you here. Right here in Bratislava! We are organized, both here and abroad. Out here we look for good dependable young men who are not afraid of anything."

"I'm not afraid. But you'd have to tell me more, and we'd have to become better acquainted."

"Here is sufficient proof. Do you recognize these names?"

Ludo looked the evidence over. There was a queer sort of legitimacy about it, but it contained some proof. It contained a snapshot of Cyril. Underneath was a statement of four people whose names Ludo well remembered; and there was even a seal at the end of the names. They had commissioned Cyril to represent a resistance movement, and asked all whom he approached for help.

"There—that should convince you!"

"It is sufficient. But, as you know, we have much hardship here. . . ."

"Are you thinking about money? If that's all, don't let it bother you. Look!" At this he pulled out a handful of American dollars from an inner coat pocket.

"From all indications, they outfitted you well."

"Well? Princely! Who is there to help you if not those Americans? They uphold us, our faith. They are relatives and sleep not; but we must co-operate with them."

"Come tomorrow, Cyril. I'll give you my answer then."

"Good! But tell no one about this talk. Don't even dream of telling it to anyone. For then your mother, Andrej, myself and a whole list of others would lose their freedom. This is strictly a secret and confidential matter."

"I've never done such work before, but am well aware of its character. I will be as silent as a fish in water."

"Do not tell even your mother anything about it."

"Rest assured, Cyril, that I will not."

43

Cyril was indeed satisfied as he pleasantly strode off to the secret police, and thence to the Secretariat of the Communist Party. There he was given a folder of dollar bills and new instructions.

Ludo had thought everything over, but it never occurred to him that Cyril might be in the service of Communists. He had heard that Slovak exiles were organizing, that they had connections with Americans, British, and French. Cyril talked so convincingly and seemed so enthusiastic about the Slovak cause, that he was convinced an honest man had come to invite him to do good work.

Ludo believed and anxiously waited the morrow when Cyril was to come for the answer. Ludo gave it to him—a favorable and a positive one. He had joined the services of the resistance movement.

"Now you have become one of us. This means both distinction and obligation."

"I appreciate this, and will do all that is in my power to fulfill my duty."

"Do you recognize the name Dubovan?"

"The name, and several people bearing that name."

"Andrej told me that you were good friends with Father Pavol, and that you were also acquainted with František Dubovan of Lipiny."

"Both of them are my distant relatives."

"So much the better. This will be your first assignment. Father Pavol is a feared adversary of Communists. František Dubovan is also upright and courageous. Dubovan upholds Father Pavol, and also has a younger brother in the West."

"Did you meet him?"

"Not yet, but I will go to see him. He sent a message through Andrej that, if any of us should visit Bratislava or Slovakia at all, to be sure to see his brother and ask for help."

"What kind of help would he need?"

"He needs money."

"But you yourself said that you get sufficient help from Americans."

"That's true. But Dubovan is a politician and would rather stand on his own feet. And although he has a share in the property at home, he is willing to let it go. His brother František is supposed to help him out in this matter. And as Dubovan has great influence among exiles in the West, he needs help from all of us. I took it on myself to find someone who would go to see his brother about it. Would you go?"

"I'd be glad to. But I have no credentials."

"Now that *is* a problem. We are not so far from Bratislava but that we can get credentials every day. I got one less than a month ago, and it's still good for ten days."

"Who gave it to you?"

"Credit for that goes to a good underground movement. We have our men at police headquarters. When conditions quiet down, I think we will have even more. But right now, credentials are curtailed, because the trials of the bishops are going on and police fear that too many people crowd into Bratislava."

"Are they afraid?"

"That they are! For the people follow the leadership of the bishops, even as they had followed that of Tiso."

"What shall we do, then?"

"I really don't know what would be the best course to follow. But wait! Could you give me a letter for František Dubovan so that I can take it to Lipiny?"

"That's not a bad idea. You have credentials, so why not go ahead?"

Ludo wrote out a letter, and Cyril was satisfied with it. The police were happy about it, too. They gave Cyril money for the journey and new instructions for winning over Dubovan.

The town of Lipiny was not large, but it was beautiful. Clean and built up, with a fine community and culture hall. It had a big church, school and rectory, several business establishments, and a brick yard. Formerly, it had also contained a distillery. But now the communists took all business to their own collective distilleries.

This lessened town wages; and the potatoes which had

formerly been changed into alcohol at the home distillery now had to be hauled to the county center. The town of Lipiny was changed.

But there were also other changes. The notary and all teachers had been removed and the gendarmes replaced with police. The cultural hall had been changed into a "Hall of People's Enlightenment." Formerly, fine plays had been conducted there, and youth had had its entertainments. Now only Soviet films were shown.

Everything is strange. All the old familiar faces that had helped the people of Lipiny are gone, with the exception of the old pastor, Father Strelák. Now everything centers about the rectory. But frequent reviews and investigations have been conducted even there. Father Strelák carries on his usual visits, now talking to one, then to another. For he loves his parishioners and bears their trials with them.

Farm homes are not as happy as they once had been. Formerly, people enjoyed themselves at weddings and christenings, but now everything is quieted down. Almost every second home has someone missing. Some have fled beyond the borders; others have been imprisoned; and still others have to look for work elsewhere. The town is desolate. Farms are collectivized.

Lipinites do not trust their new masters; neither do they look up to the new teachers, for they are communists. They avoid the militia and have already twice splattered the "Hall of People's Enlightenment" with mud. Only the church is their safeguard and refuge. The church and Mr. Dubovan— who has not lost his nerve and ever speaks up fearlessly when either the police strike or the raging communist teachers vent their gall on children and parents. They go to Dubovan and tell him their grievances, and he always has a remedy.

Even now two brothers were at Dubovan's home. They had come to seek advice, for collective farms under the hills extended to their property boundary. They feared for their land, their homestead. They didn't want to lose it. "We will not allow it to be collectivized. We are willing to give the State a greater share of our crop, but we intend to cultivate our own land."

"You think correctly. That is as it should be. Do not give up your land—unless they take it by force. It would be hard for you to do anything against force. But we will not give the communists anything just for the asking. We will defend our most productive fields. If they want anything, let them change half of the pasture land into collective holdings."

Cyril interrupted this talk when he rapped and at once looked in through the half-open door. Dubovan sized up the green-eyed youth from head to foot. He did not like his looks, for he wore short trousers and his long hair was greasy.

"Are you from town, young man?"

"Directly from Bratislava, Mr. Dubovan. But go right ahead and finish your business. For I have plenty of time to wait."

"Good neighbors, we will give this matter more consideration tomorrow." Thus he quickly dismissed the friends who had come for advice.

"What good brought you to Lipiny?"

"There's plenty of work to be done. The elders cannot keep up with it, so they send out young people."

"And who sent you to inquire about me? Authorities? Police?"

"Not at all. Your own brother sent you a message; and behold, here is a letter from your relative."

Cyril handed over Ludo's letter. Dubovan read it over carefully, pronouncing the signature out loud. Then he held the letter in his hand.

"Young man, Ludo is but a distant relative and has never written to me before. Therefore, I cannot tell whether this letter is genuine or not. That you are supposed to have come from Germany means nothing at all. You never saw my brother; and even if you had, I have my rights one way, my brother another way."

"Surely you will not refuse to help your own brother?"

"I will neither refuse, nor will I help. For you are no guarantee that he would get such help. Even at that, it is not easy for me to help. I own less and less every day. I have many obligations, am getting older and weaker, have no one

47

to work the field, and my son earns only enough to keep us existing."

"Surely it's not as bad as all that," commented Cyril.

"No, we are not yet dying of hunger. And communists—not farmers—will reap the last harvest of misery," was Dubovan's proud answer.

"Well, what are you going to do about it, Uncle Dubovan?" asked Cyril at length.

"How should it be? I told you clearly that I can give nothing and will give nothing. For I do not intend to fashion a whip for my own hide."

"But you should! Others have contributed."

"How much have you collected thus far?"

"Ten thousand crowns and five hundred dollars."

"Quit your kidding! Who would contribute dollars?"

"Our people have them. They get them from America and save them for a rainy day."

"It's not a question of them having dollars. But that they would just hand them over to you, that I do not believe. Admit where you grabbed up so much money."

Cyril did not expect such a question, and was taken aback for a moment, but he shortly regained his wits. He swore upon his soul that he had visited twenty people and all had given money.

"But that you may not deny it, give me a receipt for three hundred crowns and I will also give."

Cyril handed over a receipt in exchange for the money. Dubovan gave the money in order to get rid of him, and thought he would have peace.

Cyril left, but did not go back to Bratislava at once. He would stop along the way and engage people in conversation. Next day three of the townsmen came to Dubovan and inquired what kind of guest he had had at his place the previous evening. They told him that he was very curious about the rest of Dubovan's relatives, and about his contacts with the rectory. Cyril had asked about Father Pavol, and whether Dubovan intended to follow his brother.

"Where would I go in my old age?" sighed Dubovan.

"Even though I would like to go very much, for nothing good awaits us here. We will live through much of it; but you young people will experience much more."

"You shouldn't be downhearted, Uncle Dubovan," remonstrated a neighbor.

"You well know that I'm not faltering, but I foresee that it's going to be bad. Worse than it is today. That is not being downhearted, for we must realize what awaits us. What we are prepared for is much easier to bear, even under greater hardships."

"You are right, Uncle. Who knows what that green-eyed fellow might have wanted?"

"To extort money from people. There are many tramps like that. And who knows whether he was not directed here by Communists? He said that he came from Germany and knew such and such individuals. Anyone could tell such tales. Racketeers who do not want to work for a living serve the devil by inventing such stories, and try to fool even older people."

"Time will tell who he was," said a hillside neighbor. "One thing is certain—he stopped a lot with people and talked to women. He walked rather sure of himself from your place to the station."

Cyril did get safely by, even to Bratislava; thence to the opposite side of the Danube. He visited Ludo again and wanted to work out a visit to Father Pavol, also. But Ludo stalled him, for he had already received a letter from František Dubovan, telling him to be careful and to watch Cyril's every step.

Ludo promised to go later even to Zemianska Huta after Father Pavol.

Cyril was apparently satisfied.

Prohibited Pilgrimages

MICHAL SLOBODNIK, an old sexton and prayer leader at pilgrimages, came to Dubovan for advice. The people wanted to go to the Staré Hory again, but didn't know how to arrange it. Last year they had had a special train; this year a neighboring parish was said to have gotten one—after a lot of begging. But they had to wait two hours at the first stop. Then, somewhere out in the country, something was "damaged," and they waited three more hours. They started out again; but just as they began to sing, the conductor announced that the train would be unable to proceed any further.

They still had a two hours' walk to reach the place. They would have reached it after the solemn mass was over, so they couldn't make the pilgrimage. Hence, they got off at a neighboring village and sought out a church; and then they returned home sorrowfully.

"This had to happen to us today, when we had the pilgrimage so well organized," observed Marta Spodniačka.

"Something similar happened last Sunday also—only the other way around. First, they stopped because something was 'damaged' on the engine; later, they stopped again, for some unknown reason. They finally reached the pilgrimage, but the sermon and half of the mass was already over." So spoke the elder neighbor Martin.

Others also added their comments: "Nothing good will

come of it." "Such things do not happen by chance."

Some went to see the pastor, in order to get his advice. He lost himself in contemplation and did not reply at once. When he finally spoke, it was only in comforting words: "We will go in October and organize our pilgrimage even better."

"And what are we going to do about it?" asked Slobodník of Dubovan.

Dubovan had considered everything that had happened in these pilgrimages. And he had a ready answer for Slobodník.

"We will contact the authorities about it. I've never yet read anywhere that pilgrimages are forbidden and trains are restricted. So we'll ask for a good engine and plenty of cars, for we are going to have a big pilgrimage."

They decided to approach the authorities next morning.

But when the commissar learned that they had come to see him about a pilgrimage, he kept them waiting for an hour. When he finally called them in, it was evident from his expression that he knew who they were and considered them his enemies. In former times, and in such cases, the people in office would ask: "What would you wish?"

But this ill-mannered fellow crossly shouted at them: "Who sent you here?"

"We came to see you about an affair that concerns parishioners," replied Slobodník.

"Then you have the wrong street and house number. What have I to do with parishioners?"

"Much, sir," answered Dubovan.

"Much and nothing!" retorted the commissar. "But what is it that you want? Don't hold me up long, for I have a lot of work to do. My interest in working people means more to me than your parish petitions."

"We came to get precise information about getting a pilgrimage train. We'd like to make a pilgrimage to Staré Hory in about two or three weeks, before the end of May at the latest."

"And who sent you out to inquire about it?"

"We set out of our own accord."

"Why didn't you hand in your request last winter?"

"We didn't know about it at that time. Moreover, we thought that if people from the neighboring parish could get a train, we could get one also. For our fidelity to the faith is as good as theirs."

"It's not that easy," answered the commissar, biting into his black mustache. "You know that the war has been over but a few years. Much was destroyed, and but little has been repaired thus far. Our first concern is for freight cars to bring edibles in. Trains are also needed to transport workers to factories. And then what's left for such vain ostentations as your pilgrimages?"

"Pilgrimages are no vanity, sir," interposed Dubovan. "We used to make them even when there were very few trains. We'd go walking, and thus fulfill our obligation."

The commissar had to make a phone call, so he stepped out to the next room.

"What will we do?" asked Slobodník of Dubovan. "There's but little hope of success."

"We will insist on getting a train. If he rejects our petition outright, then we can arrange to make it on foot. It takes two days to get to Staré Hory. Ten years ago I made such a pilgrimage in company with several hundred parishioners from our parish and the neighboring one. I can do it again."

Dubovan's talk was encouraging, and Slobodník agreed. They decided to keep after the commissar till he gave them a definite answer.

The commissar returned. "We're not going to wrangle over this as though we were at a market. I have a lot of responsibility. I told you that there are no great hopes for getting a train."

"But we'd like to have you arrange for one some way," Slobodník dared to suggest.

"I haven't that much power. Neither can I spare you workers to prepare a special train, and forego patriotic work that awaits us the next three Sundays, just because candle

52

ladies and stooped peasants want to pray, and so hinder those who live by work, not by prayer."

"Prayer is a holy idea. Our people are God-fearing. They have lived for over eleven hundred years not only by drudgery, but also by prayer. It has always brought us the blessings of heaven."

"Then ask heaven to get you a train! Why follow me and other comrades around?"

The debate was getting to be acrimonious. Neither Slobodník nor Dubovan had any hopes that their desire would be granted.

"Come back in about a week or ten days. Maybe we'll know more by that time," said the surly commissar with finality.

"But we'd like to make that pilgrimage in May," Dubovan dared to remind him.

"Go ahead and make one, even today. Who's holding you back? You're no good for work any more, anyhow. But hypocrites are not going to order me around! That's final. I have my regulations, my party; you have your priests and pilgrimages. I said—in ten days. . . ."

Slobodník and Dubovan were sad. They realized that things were not as they should be.

"It doesn't seem to do us any good, and we'll hardly get that train," said Slobodník.

"Let's not lose hope. If this rascal does not grant our request, we will go further. The offices are full of these red mice, but we can yet find our man. Surely, someone will advise us where to turn and how to go about it." This was Dubovan's answer.

They had done a lot of consultation; but even on the ninth day no one could give them a better suggestion than to go back to the commissar who had kicked them out of his office. Back they went, almost convinced that the pilgrimage would be a failure. They prepared the people accordingly, intending to make the pilgrimage on foot.

They came back to the commissariat.

"You here again?" queried the comrade.

"You told us to come back. We came back to find out whether you will give us a train to get to Staré Hory."

"I talked it over with the comrades at the ministry. They decided to give you a train. But I warn you that it will be bad for you if you do not fill it. And if you attract all kinds of thieves and enemies of working people, it will be all the worse. Our government works only for the people. I want you to understand that."

"We will do what we can," offered Slobodník.

"Not what you can, but what our party *wants,* understand? That's my responsibility. Good luck!"

"Maybe it will be good luck yet," said Slobodník to Dubovan when they were out on the street and pulling their hats down over sweated brows.

"I haven't any too good a hope, my godfather. To me it seems that this 'our party' and the police are taking the place of the church and our priests. And that is bad."

"We've got our train. Now we must prepare ourselves for the pilgrimage," said the sexton and prayer leader.

"Yes. The parishioners are curious about it. We've attained our main objective; we will be at Staré Hory in May. Our desire will be achieved."

Slobodník and Dubovan now had their hands full. Others soon joined them, elders as well as younger men. The rector announced the pilgrimage twice from the pulpit, and sent out the servers to every home telling the people to get ready if they wanted to come along.

The week before the pilgrimage was a busy one, for all the housewives were industriously engaged in washing. Their garden lines were adorned with their costumes—yellow and red colors predominated, and golden cloth flowed through as though it had been poured out. But it was only the skillful hands of peasant women, working during long winter nights, that had conjured up such arts with needle and thread.

The parishioners met at the church for three nights in succession. They decided who was going to do the intoning, and how they would arrange themselves. The cross again was to lead the procession, the youth behind it with banners, then women, and finally the men.

The band was on hand. There were thirty-six men in full force, firmly holding their brass instruments. The church resounded as though it were confirmation time or the Christmas season, and there was great joy among the parishioners. The pilgrimage was all they could talk about.

"And who will preach at the Staré Hory?" was the question asked.

The rector answered: "I have received a letter from Staré Hory informing me that a good preacher would be provided, and that we have nothing to worry about. I will go along with you. We are going to pray during the journey. I will help with confessions and will say a low mass."

The train was scheduled to leave on Saturday night. On Friday Slobodník consulted Dubovan and called on three elderly men. They talked among themselves and said nothing to anyone else. They were all trustworthy parishioners and deserving members.

On Saturday Slobodník interviewed four men there before anyone else had arrived at the train. And he had more than that: three great crosses were propped up against the steps. They were about the size of the cross that Jesus bore. That was Slobodník's surprise, and the parishioners accepted his idea with great enthusiasm. But one said: "We should have marched behind those crosses in procession from the church, instead of going as usual, behind one small cross carried by a server."

Slobodník called this parishioner aside and, in a half-whisper, explained: "That's the way it *was* going to be, but last night Dubovan came over to inform me that the militia was going to spy on us. Therefore, to avoid the worst at the onset, we decided to make this manifestation at Staré Hory. Don't worry, Janko, everything will be in order. As I see it, one of these militia men is here with us. The scoundrel had the nerve to disguise himself in our costume, in order to mingle unnoticed among the pilgrims."

Everything was now in order and the pilgrims boarded

55

the train. Just before the start, male and female voices resounded with the hymn: "Chosen before all ages, Queen of Angels!"

A rosary followed this hymn; and when it was completed, there were more Slovak pilgrimage hymns, Slobodník and Dubovan intoning.

The disguised militia man in the corner forced himself to sing and pray, but somehow he couldn't make a proper impression. A neighboring lady noticed that he didn't even have a rosary and did not sing aloud. Everything seemed to have stuck in his throat. His eyes were slant and had bags under them. Who knows where he had been the night before?

Some parishioners informed Slobodník and his godfather Dubovan that they thought one of these "new" police, or whatever you call them, was in their midst. Thus far he had never attended church services—and here, all of a sudden, he goes on a pilgrimage!

Slobodník, who rode in the second car, told the men to be ever at his heels. "Watch his every move on the train, then at Staré Hory; keep your eyes on him till we get back.

"He will not foil our plans. Even if they should send him help, we will accomplish our mission. Since we have the train, we will make this pilgrimage and show everyone what's in our hearts and what our faith is made of. We are not ashamed of our church and our devotion to the Blessed Virgin."

The train neared its destination, and the rector reminded the servers to dress up. In five minutes twelve servers, all wearing white gloves, entered.

The pilgrims were now getting off. First, came the priest. A fresh breeze rustled his gray hair as he looked over the station from the steps. It seemed as though he were searching for someone there. But then he quickly looked underfoot to step down safely.

Slobodník and Dubovan followed the rector; then servers with a cross; three men, each with a great cross; the youth; and finally, the whole crowd poured out of the train.

The great throng filled the station. Then they filed in front of it, four deep. In the center was a great cross, with servers and the rector behind it. Each group carried banners.

Everyone was in native costume. A great variety of colors decorated the scene. Hundreds of boots glittered, hundreds of prayer books were enthroned on the hands of peasants, their wives and their children, and hundreds of pairs of beads hung on heavy hands. The small crosses dangling from the beads were badges of the continuous way of the cross of this faithful people. The great crosses were a sign that something important was taking place. Here was a public declaration, although a quiet one.

Slobodník contentedly looked over the procession as Dubovan intoned: "O sorrowful Mother Mary."

They started out reverently, marching down the village. Bells were rung in honor of the pilgrims; and the town rector, with servers and banners, came to meet them. This made the procession one cross and four banners longer.

"Now you can wonder at it, Commissar!" thought Slobodník to himself. "Observe your materialistic world which places so many obstacles in our way. Wonder, all of you who have not learned to believe! Rave, ye powers of darkness, for we are the masters here!"

They finally arrived before the pilgrimage church. There they found many devout faithful gathered together from all parts. The pilgrims entered the church, prayed, and again sang a hymn: "A Rose Bloomed in the Staré Hory Church."

In a while it was announced that a field mass with sermon would take place. In addition, there would be low masses at all the altars of the church.

They all went out, for the weather was fine. The sun warmed them pleasantly. Dean Sutovský said the mass. Four bands alternately played Slovak religious hymns. The people sang in a body. Surrounding hills resounded, and the echo carried far down the dale. Sturec Hill witnessed an unheard-of church celebration.

The mass had scarcely begun when one of the men came running up to Slobodník, drew him by the cape, and whispered: "I saw how that rascal of a militia man went off to town. He returned after a little while—but not alone. With him were four civilians."

"Let's take courage, Jožko," answered Slobodník. "We are here, and we will hold out and return just as solemnly as we came."

Slobodník sang and prayed, but somehow his left eye twitched.

"Maybe a sign? A *bad* sign? But you are a man! You were not afraid of the commissar and organized everything. Will you now take notice of the twitching of one little nerve? Pray and defeat the devils! . . ."

He prayed contentedly. Following the gospel the dean announced that the sermon would take place after mass, but he did not give the name of the preacher.

They awaited the sermon. After mass the deacon, a priest unknown to the pilgrims, introduced the preacher. He was the noted apostate Alexander Norák, who publicly and energetically espoused the Communist Party, attended its "Peace" conferences, issued reports, threatened the Vatican, and publicly denounced the Holy Father as an ally of the Wall Street incendiaries of a new war and of capitalistic extortioners of the working masses.

The crowd stirred. Some called out half-aloud: "We don't want a renegade! Where have our priests gone to?"

"Be quiet, faithful Christians, and listen to the preacher," sounded the voice of the one who had introduced Norák.

Some quieted down, but a majority grumbled and many left at once. Some remained only out of curiosity. They hadn't heard Norák yet. They were curious to know whether a person in priestly vestments was capable of running down the church and praising Communism.

They soon found out. Norák preached on the theme: "Give to God what is God's and to Caesar what is Caesar's."

"To God what is God's. That means that the church, our heart, our prayers and our reverence belong to God. But to God and his servants, the Pope, bishops and priests does not belong the idea of joining those who twisted the laws of God,

58

who prepare for a new war, who manufactured the most horrible weapons and also made use of bacteriological warfare. And that is the downfall of Christianity, when Rome unites with those who oppose peace movements and prepare to conquer the world with dollars. This is where the Vatican has made a mistake. This was not the idea of Christ's teaching, nor the idea of the life of true Christians."

Slobodník listened, but tears welled up in his eyes. The disguised militia man was standing on the side, watching Slobodník. Another one took Dubovan under his observation.

Norák continued: "The West proclaims democracy, but comes up with the harshest kind of slavery. America lords it over fifteen million colored people, does not consider Indians equal citizens, and is preparing for plunder in Asia and also here in Europe. For dollars she buys saleable souls, weakling governments who serve America even as other governments formerly served the fascists. America with her aggression is not far from bringing about the harshest kind of fascism.

"Now look on the other side of the picture, at the East— our native brothers, Slav Russians, and their genius of a leader and protector of all of us here in the East and the hope of those in the West, Josef Vissarionovich Stalin! He fulfills the principle, 'Give God what is God's, and Caesar what is Caesar's,' in the proper sense of the text. He looks not for allies among those who live off working people, but himself works for the people. He gives bread, he gives a program, and leads us all to peace."

"You are Satan, and hell gave birth to your mother!" said Dubovan to himself. He jerked his neighbor by the sleeve and motioned with his right hand for him to go. This neighbor jerked another neighbor, and in a little while the whole gathering moved, with Slobodník and Dubovan in front.

They went around the church. They sang Marian songs and, in a little while, realized what kind of manhood it was that was leading them. They arranged themselves behind the church. Then the gray-haired Rector Strelák knelt down before the middle cross and prayed: "We ask heaven and the Blessed Virgin's forgiveness for all the insults which are committed throughout the world."

The people understood and prayed aloud. Surely, heaven must have heard this prayer directly. When he had finished, Strelák made another intention: "Let us pray for the Holy Father and the whole church."

The third intention was for martyrs and those in suffering.

Strelák had just finished, and the faithful were about to say "Amen," when four fully armed militia men jumped the priest. One of them hit him with his fist straight in the face, while the others manacled him.

"People! This is more than blasphemy. This is the greatest of insults!" came from the crowd. "We will not give up our priests!" "Let's be true heroes. Let them shoot us all—but they're not going to murder our priests."

And already some thirty men had the militia men surrounded. They crowded them so hard that they had no chance to defend themselves. Some took charge of the militia men, while others returned Rector Strelák back before the three crosses.

"Let us pray . . ." began Strelák, and Slobodník added: "For America and for our Slovak-American brothers and sisters!"

"Who was that?" asked a gruff voice from the right side of the church. Norák came along, accompanied by more militia men. Behind them was a whole regiment, all fully armed.

Fifty men stepped out of the crowd at once and called, "It was I!"

Out of the crowd, other voices followed: "I'm for it, too. I also would have asked for such a prayer!"

But the disguised militia man had been spying on Slobodník. He had followed his every move and caught his every word. He well knew that it was Slobodník who had asked the people to pray for American Slovaks.

The big eyed militia man in costume jumped beside Slobodník and faced the crowd. When the other militia men were already on hand, he indicated that Slobodník was the greatest culprit.

"He it is! Rebel and worker's enemy Number One! He persuaded Strelák to make this pilgrimage. Slobodník is his name. Hold him fast!"

The militia men did their duty. A hundred machine guns were trained on the pilgrims. One commanded: "Anyone who moves will be killed, do you understand?"

A great rustle was the response.

But the pilgrims could not help themselves. Strelák was tied up again, as also were all the other priests who had remained faithful to the church and their people. They took Slobodník and some eight men and women who had cried out when Strelák had been attacked.

The journey home was made on foot. The appeals of the praying pilgrims were heard among the century-old oaks. They were not allowed to travel in groups of more than five.

Sister Katarína

THERE WERE two Sisters-in-religion from Dubovan's village in the Vincentian Convent. One of them was his own sister, who had taken the religious name of Anna. The other one was Katarína, whose home had once been the fourth house from Dubovan's. Parishioners had heard a lot from these Sisters formerly while there was still freedom. But lately, visits were progressively harder to get. Anna, who was a nurse, had been transferred to another town; Katarína, who had been a professor, in time was also placed in a hospital.

This turn of events came suddenly, but Katarína had expected them. Her students had long been bringing her queer reports from town. They talked of how pressure had been used to force state employees to join the Communist Party; how some had been deprived of their business establishments, others of their land; how some had been imprisoned, others taken to unknown destinations.

Sister Katarína quietly listened to her students' reports;

and when they complained, she encouraged them with good advice. When matters became worse, even parents came to see her. Sister Katarína now preferred to take her friends to a closed classroom, in order to be less conspicuous.

Even when she stopped teaching—for the government took over the schools—Sister Katarína was visited by acquaintances. She herself was a peasant's daughter, understanding every heart beat of her good and devout people. Consequently, she couldn't help being solicitous for her own. In fact, she took such an interest that those whose means would allow sent their daughters to Katarína for night courses.

But nothing escaped the communists. Once little Marienka came running to the convent, all out of breath, and crying.

"What goes on, Marienka?" asked Sister Katarína.

"They have taken my dad away! Mother told me that I can no longer attend school with you, for she has nothing to help the convent with. She has no work; and even before that, the state took over our business establishment. What are we to do?"

"Don't worry, Marienka. As long as I have two good hands, I will look after you. Only come to school tomorrow night. I will arrange for everything with Sister Superior. We are poor, and you have nothing except your faith, so why shouldn't we help each other mutually?"

Marienka threw herself into the Sister's arms and cried with joy.

Sometime later little Petrík came to see Katarína, for his mother had died and his dad was in a hospital. He asked whether Katarína could arrange to have his father transferred to the hospital. This was accomplished.

Students who had been expelled from the university also came. They were brothers of the girls that Katarína taught. She helped them out. She sent them to monasteries and gave them addresses of courageous youths who had a secret hiding place.

Once a three-member commission from her own village sought her out. It was right after the horrible happenings at

Staré Hory. It didn't take Katarína long to give them sound advice: "Hold together with Dubovan, and also get younger men to join you, to take Dubovan's place if necessary."

Other Sisters who had studied with her at the university, and had met her at the various courses given by the state for the professors, also called on Katarína. They wanted advice concerning the future.

"We will not give up, but remain faithful to the vows we took. And we will keep on helping. In these days we cannot consider what we are according to title and education. We must take a realistic view of how the godless and unfeeling communists try to deprive our Slovak people of their faith; how they take our priests and drag away our best people; how those that are most honorable must hide in secret caves or flee across borders; how marriages are disrupted and our youth ruined."

"Correct, correct, Katarína! For we think the same way, and only wanted your opinion, because you are more experienced and come in contact with the public more frequently."

Katarína had her Superior's permission to visit private homes urgently in need of help. She would bring food for little children and aged sickly people to one place; clothing, linen or other things, donated by the convent or spared from the hospital, to another.

Once Katarína went to a well-known home. She did not even get to knock. She was carrying a bundle of clothing under her arm for an elderly acquaintance who was in bed weakened with hunger and sickness.

A policeman greeted Katarína at the threshold.

"What do you want?"

"I am coming to visit the sick lady."

"This late at night?"

"Whenever I get time, and the need requires it."

"What are you carrying?"

"Just a little clothing, for I know that the sick lady hasn't much."

"And you have?"

"No, but something can always be found in a convent."

"Haven't you any other plans? I also came here to meet someone. I'm waiting for young Vinco."

"Vinco?"

"Don't pretend, Sister. I think you know him well."

"I've heard about him, but have never met him."

"How long have you been visiting this home?"

"About three weeks."

"This is very, very interesting."

With his last words, the policeman glanced at the Sister significantly, as if to say; "You will not escape us."

And Sister Katarína realized it, but gave no external indication of her awareness. She did not even flick an eyebrow. Pretending unconcern, she crossed the threshold and greeted the sick lady. She asked about her condition, gave her the package, and left after a while, promising to return again.

But she did not return. Not that she didn't want to, but because Vinco's mother died. Only from hills did Vinco send messages to his friends. He also sent Katarína one. He thanked her for attending to his mother and confided to her his plans. Vinco also gave Katarína two town names by the same messenger.

Now Katarína had two additional charges. It was easier for her, as the two concerned were young girls who could move about freely and meet the Sister wherever it was most convenient—once in the sacristy; another time beside the cloister chapel; again at the cathedral vestibule; and then again at the hospital. One of these girls came to the hospital for a general checkup, and Katarína was able to talk everything over with her. She listened as the "patient" unfolded all the plans of the youth, and she in turn told her of the situation in the convent, in the hospital, and about teachers and professors.

The young girl was not so much concerned about names as she was to understand the circumstances under which the people existed. And she strove to remember every need, how individuals were tracked down, and those who were already imprisoned.

Katarína was on the alert, but when she became convinced that the girl was truly in the service of an anticommunist cell, she talked more freely.

But the Sister did not reveal even now the most important factors. That was unnecessary, for the people who were in the greatest danger were already being helped by her friends in the city. She herself helped some of them. Even as her good friend Sister Cecília, in another hospital and of a different religious order, had been doing right along.

Good work is like a sweet prayer. It unites people and spreads from person to person. The Sisters had plenty of courage. For what they couldn't accomplish with their hands, they prayed for daily before the altar and in their cells.

Such were Katarína and many of her fellow Sisters-in-religion. There were the prominent ones, the less prominent ones, and those entirely "forgotten." People were unconscious of them, but God knew their intentions, considered their acts, and took note of every step.

But even as others noticed the Sisters, so did the communist police. Katarína was taken under observation, especially after the time the policeman had met her at Vinco's sick mother's home. At first she was unconscious of this, for the police were cautious. But once two middle-aged men, dressed in rather shabby clothing, came to the hospital. They wanted to meet Katarína, so she came and introduced herself to them.

These men posed as anticommunist workers, but said little of their activity. Outside of mentioning Vinco's name, they did not even give the slogan or furnish convincing evidence that they were devoted to this work. For Sister Katarína it was enough. She was careful. When they asked her whom she had saved lately, she pretended not to know of anything or anybody. For she realized that this could be a trap set for her. She had heard of cases where the secret police would enter into just such conversations.

And she had guessed right. On the following day, uniformed police arrived, five of them, fully armed and in an auto. They broke into Katarína's cell and searched her. But they found only prayer books and books of devotion, nothing else. However, they looked them over to see when and where they had been published. But as they had not been published under communist auspices, they took them along without giving anyone any explanation. One of the men struck the statuettes of the Blessed Virgin and Saint Theresa with a blackjack, knocking them to the floor. Then he reached up for the cross, took it off the wall, and threw it under the bed.

At this outrage, Katarína cried out in protest: "Rather bind and kill me than offend God that way!"

At this the communist youth started laughing satanically, and one of them said to her triumphantly: "Take it easy, ungovernable woman; we know what kind of a bird you are. We know you better than you think we do. We're not going to consult and debate here at all. Come along with us!"

"Where to?"

"Just to the ground floor. We will tell your Superior in your presence that this is the last warning."

They took her down and told the Sister Superior that she would be held responsible for Katarína's every step. "If she leaves the hospital at all, she will be punished according to the justice of the people's democracy."

"Do you understand?" asked one of the police in a harsh voice.

"I understand. But we have our convent regulations and are still subject to church law."

"There are no laws above the laws of our just government. Dare to conduct yourselves otherwise—and you shall see!"

The police slammed the door and left.

"What do you think about it, venerable Mother?" asked Katarína when the police were gone.

"Just as I've always thought. Our vows and regulations bind us, and that is all there is to it."

"I thank you. I thought the same way, and am glad that I didn't have to beg you not to remind me of the police regulations."

"Nothing of the kind, Katarína. We understand each other perfectly, and both of us are conscious of our obligations. Let's continue fulfilling them in resignation to God's will."

Katarína continued doing her usual work just as before

the police visit. But not for long. They must have seen her again somewhere in town.

Katarína had just returned to the hospital when three policemen came and ordered her into a car.

She knelt down before the Mother Superior for her blessing and received it.

Then the two religious women embraced each other. Mother Superior was crying, but Katarína controlled herself. She gave her Superior a look as though lightning had struck. It was a sign that they understood each other and would continue to do so.

They took Katarína away to another town and to a strange hospital, for they needed nurses. But there were no Sisters in this hospital, and the manager was a coarse person. Loyal to the regime, he leered at Katarína and greeted her in an unfriendly manner: "We have no Sisters in our hospital, and I don't want you to create a novelty. Get rid of that disturbing attire and clothe yourself as a regular nurse."

"Is that why you had me called here, Mr. Manager?"

"For that very reason. I have said what I have to say. I think you understood me."

"I understand, but . . ."

"What do you mean? I give orders here! And if I can't prevail over one nurse to observe order in this hospital, everything will be in confusion."

"I submit to order and will tend the sick diligently. But I will not remove my habit. I cannot and will not allow it. My conscience, vows, and oaths are most sacred to me. I will not betray nor relinquish that which designates me as a servant of the Lord."

"We'll see to that," angrily answered the manager.

At this he motioned to a secular nurse to guide Katarína to a room. Sister Katarína found herself in a small room with four beds in it.

She looked over the walls. She did not find there what she was looking for—no cross, not a holy picture! There were pictures of communist leaders and broad inscriptions: "Let us fulfill the quota!" "Long live the liberator of all Slavs, Josef Stalin!" "Work for Peace!" "With Soviets Against Capitalistic Tyrants!" "Down with the Vatican!"

"This is no place for me," said Katarína when she looked about the room and read the slogans.

"Yes, indeed it is," said a nurse. "We will live together here, as faithful comrades."

"This room, with its blasphemous slogans, offends me."

"Make nothing of it, comrade! Don't read them, and lower your eyes wherever you will. I don't read them either; but for all that, I do not lean over to the other side. Communists gave me a job, so I'm faithful to them as long as I don't resist."

"I cannot and will not be that way," answered Sister Katarína.

"You will get used to it, even as I did and many others."

Just then three other nurses entered. One of them stepped directly in front of Katarína, touched her habit disdainfully, and said with contempt: "We do not need such vanity here. This room is not a convent. Read, comrade, there on the wall, and conduct yourself accordingly. I am responsible for order here. There in the closet is clothing for a regular nurse. Pick out some clothes for yourself and throw off what they pasted on you at the convent."

"Your talk is blasphemous," quietly answered Katarína.

"This is neither a church nor a convent, and no Dark Age society! Here we work, and you will be rewarded for what you do. But you must obey."

"And who will force me to?"

Katarína cast her eyes down, and it seemed that she was reconsidering. But she was praying, and her right hand reached down for her great rosary.

The unruly nurse then grabbed Katarína by the left hand and led her to the closet. She told her to open it, but Katarína would not listen. Neither did she allow herself to be ordered by the first command that the nurse gave her.

"You will not get me to do that. This habit has suited me

for many years, and will continue to satisfy me. In it I pray; in it I work; and if it be God's will, in it I will die."

"This hypocrisy will not help you, comrade. Either you obey, or we will get new orders."

"May it happen as it will. I will not give up my rights voluntarily. I will not consent to anyone in this world to do what is against my religious regulations."

"That we shall see," added the nurse in a raised, squeaky voice. "I will give you one hour. This is your bed. Over there in the closet, as I told you, are your clothes. I'll be back in an hour to take you to the hospital. *But in civilian dress!*"

All the nurses left the room, the mistress leaving last and banging the door. Sister Katarína was left alone.

She knelt down as though she were in a prison. The slogans above her head seemed to her like bars.

"God, what will I do?" she sighed aloud. But then quickly added: "I resign myself wholly to Thee, my Lord. I believe in Thee, I hope in Thee, I will remain your faithful servant, come what may."

It was hard for Katarína to stand up in that room. But it was much harder to make a step towards the closet. She did not go there, but to the bed. Taking her rosary crucifix into both hands, she knelt at the bed and gazed on the crucified. It seemed to her that the bed burned her elbows. But a glance at the crucifix moderated her grief, and she quieted the disturbance of her soul with prayer and meditation.

Katarína did not care what was going on, or what would happen in the near future. She decided to adhere to her habit and give in neither to the commanding comrade nor to the manager. She continued in quiet prayer during the whole hour.

Precisely in an hour, the commanding nurse rushed into the room, shoving another comrade before her.

"You, here, will take charge of this Katarína—or whatever they call her."

And when she saw the Sister kneeling beside the bed, she shouted: "Is that how you obey a command, comrade?"

The Sister raised her head and bravely looked into the eyes of the mistress as she said quietly: "I obey the voice of my conscience and nothing more."

"That would be the life for you, wasting your time in the dormitory and doing as you please. But here we *work!* The government doesn't feed anyone for nothing. This holds for you also, Katarína," said the mistress in a somewhat modified tone of voice.

But even this did not affect Katarína. She did not move from the bed, neither did she intend to interfere with the talk of the communist nurse.

Katarína's calm angered the mistress. Jumping to the bed, she jerked her by the habit and ordered her to get up at once and change clothing.

"All that I can do," said the Sister, "is to put a white cloak over my religious habit, as we did in the convent hospital."

"The manager wants more than that, and so do I," said the embittered comrade. "And that—*at once!*"

A gravelike silence was the only answer the angered nurse received.

In Forced Labor

"THE GODLESS will stop for no one and at nothing," Dubovan interrupted Katarína, who had just related a part of her experiences during the past year.

"And that is not all, Uncle. I've gone through a lot more; and who knows what other religious people may have had to experience? Thank God I got by safely! I will continue to resist just as strongly in the future."

"May God help you, Sister!" added Dubovan.

He had made the trip to this district town, where Katarína was nursing in a small hospital, expressly to learn of the fate of his own sister, Anna, who was also a Vincentian and knew Sister Katarína well.

Dubovan didn't have to wait long. Although her time was

limited, she knew he was waiting for news of his own sister. "Anna," began Katarína, "conducts herself admirably. We appreciated her virtue and were inspired by her example. And those who did not know her at first began at once to idolize her. And they had reason to. She taught us a lot, and inspired us especially by one example, which speaks for the rest.

"But that I may not repeat and backtrack, I will tell everything from the beginning. When I would not give up my religious habit at the hospital, they no longer trusted me. They gave me no work, neither did I eat on the day I had my altercation with the manager and the communist spy. They put me on a truck in charge of two civilians, who took me to a great collective center. There I found several religious persons, among them Anna.

"My heart felt lighter at once. I felt almost as if I were in a convent, although things were much changed here. Everything was on a new basis, for both ourselves and the inhabitants. They chased us out to a former estate, where they allowed one room for eighteen of us. It was our kitchen, refectory, and dormitory.

"But that wasn't the worst of it. The room was quite large, and we kept it clean. It was the supervision that bothered us. There were seventeen Sisters, and the eighteenth was a queer girl who had neither education nor a decent word for anyone. She would scold and curse as she drove us to work. She laughed aloud as though demented when we would bless ourselves, and she cracked the whip when we wanted to pray aloud. Finally she announced: 'Out here we *work*—which is more than idle fingering of beads. Beads mean nothing to us.'

"It was hard for us to get used to this farm and the scoldings and threats of the girl. But we knew what to do about it. We prayed, each one for herself; and by pressing the beads that we wear with our habits, we gave each other signals, encouraging each other."

"Were you allowed to go to church?"

"At first they allowed us to go several times, even on work

71

days. Later, on Sundays only; and finally, they hindered us so that we could not go, even on Sundays and holidays. And this especially caused us to fall out of harmony with the communist control at the collective center; and we were finally forced to go to various other places.

"The work was hard. We got up at four in the morning, and at five we had to be out in the fields, working. We would dig, scatter manure, pick stones, or do any other general farm work. But with the difference that a farmer is his own boss. He plows and sows, mows and threshes when the weather is good and his strength adequate. With it he prays and encourages himself. In other words, he leads a decent life.

"But this does not apply at the collective center, and especially not for religious persons placed there for punishment. They chased us, watched whether we talked together, made fun of us; and when we scattered manure, remarked how it befitted our religious habits.

"Once it happened that a stripling, who had charge of us, picked up some manure on a fork and threw it in such a way that some fell on Anna. She lowered her eyes, but the dissolute young communist laughed uproariously and, cracking a whip, called out: 'This is but a beginning; it will get worse, comrade. Go ahead, no idling!'

"Once he would chase us; at another time he would crack the whip over our heads, forcing us constantly to work, work!

"A person enjoys working: but a religious person cannot keep it up daily for eighteen hours with but little food. The scheme of the communist officials was to exhaust us, in order to get us to make concessions. Generally, after the hardest kind of work done in rain, either directors of the collective center or special agents would try persuading us to give up our habits and work for the people to provide a more comfortable and better life.

"What they considered a more 'comfortable' existence, not one of them ever told us.

"But we knew what it meant: it was a paradise of dreams, according to Marx, Lenin and Stalin. We had had enough of it, and didn't want more.

72

"After some time, both men and women civilians joined us in the fields. We soon learned that they were Slovak farmers whose property had been confiscated. They had been convicted of rebellion for opposing the collectivization of their village. At first they had imprisoned them, then divided them among us at the collective center.

"Anna got into contact with a farm wife, who told her all while they were feeding cattle together. She also told Anna that the Communists had ordered her and the rest who came with her to persuade the Sisters to renounce religious life and to join the Communist Party. They would make us professors and teachers; give us important positions in hospitals; and such as had had no university education could start to teach at universities without any proper preparation.

" 'But you Slovak sisters have a grave responsibility before God and the Slovak people,' said this simple peasant woman to Anna. 'It would be a curse to the people if you consented to do so. Your mothers and fathers in the village expect courage and sacrifices from you. They pray for you, even as we here pray along with you. We've also lost everything. Communists have confiscated our village homesteads, but cannot rob us of our faith. If you do not permit yourselves to be overwhelmed, we will continue to perform this slavery more contentedly.'

"Stirred with emotion, Anna admitted that she had not experienced such wholesome fear and reverence even while taking solemn vows as she had when this simple Slovak woman spoke to her heart.

"And properly speaking, this message was for all of us. I also felt that it was a message from our own village. Suddenly, it took me back in spirit to the center of our own humble but self-conscious town. In it I saw the fired expressions of father, mother, sisters, brothers, uncles and aunts. The entire village flashed before my eyes. And all of them gazed intently on me, to the very depths of my soul, as it were. And their look was like that of Jesus on the cross when He entrusted His Mother to His beloved disciple John.

"Deprived of its natural leaders, robbed of its farms, business establishments, the Slovak village now looked up to us for courage and inspiration. I couldn't help but picture you heading that village, Uncle. For even though you were at the time far away from us, yet you were close in spirit. And here we had been thinking that we were the only ones carrying the cross.

"After this first talk, Anna was anxious to meet the other women who had been dragged in as slaves. And she succeeded in meeting one of them briefly, for but a moment. Sister had just finished saying, 'How do you exist?' when a rascal slashed her over the back with a whip. He had been hiding somewhere in a corner, spying on Sister Anna and her companion.

" 'We have no time for gossip, comrade! More work and less talk!'

"Rushing at her again with the whip, he spat on the ground, as if he wanted to humiliate Sister Anna even more."

"He humiliated himself, the ill-bred fellow!" said Dubovan.

"Most certainly! When, on the following Sunday, Anna slipped us a note in the chapel about what had happened to her, we became more cautious in our movements. Not for ourselves, but for the poor people who wanted to return to their children and care for them. We wanted to save them from harm.

"But very little could be hidden from the insolent communists. When they noticed how regularly we went to church, marching two by two, or how we would like to lengthen our devotions after mass, they thought up a diabolic scheme.

"They prepared quotas. Each one of us would have to do so much work each week. Naturally, rain or intense heat would prevent us from fulfilling our quota in six days. Therefore, they ordered us to work on Sundays also. We resisted as best we could. Finally, we consented to work on Sunday afternoons if we could go to Mass in the morning. Again they schemed.

"They increased our quotas; and when Sunday-afternoon

74

work became insufficient to satisfy them, they ordered us to work out in the fields and to clean stables—even on Sunday mornings. They ordered us to report at seven. We came as usual, for we always had to tend to the barns in the morning. Although they did not need all to do this work, they forced all of us to go there. This enabled us to do the work in thirty minutes, and at eight we went to church in time for Mass.

"It was now Saturday again, and the boy who had been unmercifully cracking the whip over us, and had even dared to strike Anna, announced imperiously: 'This week you have been idling around for two days because of rain. Tomorrow we work as usual. Do you understand?'

"No one answered him. He shouted and screamed, trying to get us to answer, but got none. He kept us there in the yard for half an hour, without results.

"In the morning he woke us up as usual, and again shouted that we weren't going to pray, but would have to go straight to the threshing. Everything would be threshed that day and hauled away to the main storeroom.

"He kept shouting under our windows; and the girl who was with us was also not slow to enter into obscene conversation with him, so as to get us out of the room as soon as possible. They would always do this when they needed us urgently out in the fields.

"We dressed ourselves very quickly. That night we cleaned our habits of all mud and dirt in order to be dressed a little more festively for the Lord's day. When the last Sister was ready, all of us stood at the door. Sister Anna started leading the Litany of the Sacred Heart, and all of us made the responses.

"Then Anna opened the door and crossed the threshold. We followed her. The girl didn't bother us, for we were accustomed to doing this often. The hired boy was also silent. It was only when we stopped in front of the house and continued praying louder that he cracked his whip and sent a large hunting dog after us. But the dog remained quiet. He would jump on his hind legs, but didn't open his mouth.

75

He lay on the ground; and the more the Communist rascal spurred him on, the more the dog rolled around, waggling his tail."

"That dog was smarter than his master," said Dubovan.

"That's right. Communist sadists are at times entirely demented and haven't even as much regard as a dumb animal.

"At this, however, Anna took three steps forward, stopped leading the litany, and in an even tone said: 'Unless you promise to allow us to go to church today and on next Sunday, and twice during the week to mass, and give us an opportunity for weekly confession, we do not go to the stable.'

" 'And what else would you like? To go back to the convent, I suppose!'

"Cracking the whip again, he jumped for Anna, with both fists aimed at her face. But he did not hit her, for all of us grouped about Anna and pushed aside this shameless communist. One of the Sisters stepped on his whip, the end of which lay on the ground and said: 'Not any of you will get us to do slave work if you refuse us our most natural rights.'

"The boy shouted to the girl, but she only kept running around us, laughing as though deprived of the use of reason. He commanded her to go and get help, and cried out as if calling someone. During this momentary distraction, he jerked the whip. The Sister who had stepped on it reeled a little, and he tried to hit her with his fist. But she was the more agile, and quickly joined us in the circle. We crowded facing together, and continued praying, taking notice of nothing going on. I thought this would pass and we'd be able to reason with the communists and gain our rights.

"But it didn't work. The manager of the collective center, who was a very rude person, soon arrived on the scene. He was dirty and in muddy shoes, with a greasy cap on his head. Chewing a cigarette, he leered at us.

"He cursed till it chilled us to the bone and made us say the response, 'Have mercy on us,' all the louder.

" 'Quiet, you hypocritical rabble!'

"We quieted down as Sister Anna again stepped out and said: 'Cease from offending us so grievously and from vilifying our faith!'

76

" 'Faith? Do you know what faith is? We give you a place to sleep, you are clothed, and we give you great privileges. What more do you want? Will faith feed you? Can you help the working masses with faith?'

" 'That is your doctrine. We have another teaching,' was the response from our midst.

" 'Back to work, you idlers! We have not time to waste on words. There has been enough of idling. Here we have other laws in force.'

"So raved the repulsive manager of the collective center as his hired boy again cracked the whip.

"But Sister Anna called out bravely: 'Our patience is exhausted. Give us your final word.'

" 'That was already spoken. I will not repeat,' answered the communist agent.

" 'We have also made a demand,' answered three voices simultaneously. And Anna added that we would not move till we got permission to go to church regularly.

"But this impasse was of short duration, for time was flying and they already had a plan worked out for us. The manager whispered something to the boy, who ran off to the building.

"Then, in a markedly milder tone, the manager said: 'Do not make it hard for us who are responsible for the association. I will gladly give you better meals—but obey! For we have a lot of work to do today.'

" 'We will do it tomorrow, even if we have to work till ten at night; only let us go to church today,' forcibly spoke up Sister Anna.

" 'That will not do! I can't put off the work till tomorrow. Come today.'

" 'We will not go!' was the outcry of our collective seventeen throats.

"Then the godless communist began to curse again, but we cast our eyes down and prayed. We were not left alone for long, however. Six men came and started shouting and chasing us to the stable.

"We moved, not towards the stable, but for the village. The men surrounded us, and the manager of the center, jumping in front of Sister Anna, spat on her habit.

" 'All for your greater honor and glory, O Lord,' she said; and we added: 'May God be blest!'

"But six men started forcing us with sticks and by hand towards the stable.

"It took them a long time to get us near the stable in which we worked. But by that time a truck thundered up, and a militia man jumped out of it. Raising his right hand, he said: 'All of you board the truck!'

"More militia men, with drawn revolvers, were in the truck.

"We knew that we could not resist. At length, involuntarily, and only at the third request, after repeated abuses from the militia men, did we start getting on the truck. These militia men shoved us as though we were but dumb animals.

"It turned out to be a sad Sunday. We cried bitterly on the truck as the dust filled our eyes and cut us off from the sight of the militia men."

Dubovan, who had attentively followed every word, interrupted Sister Katarína, saying: "Whom God loveth, him He chastiseth."

"We did not know where they were taking us to," continued Katarína. "But we offered up all our grief in expiation for missing mass that day. At nightfall they unloaded us at some sort of an old shed, where we slept on bare ground. Communists alternated in guarding us. They would flash lights into our faces and kept going around us. They guarded us closely to see that we were not talking, or perhaps to see if we were scheming to escape.

"But where would defenseless and weak women flee?

"There was but little to eat. Dry bread and a little sour milk, nothing more. But we ate even that thankfully, for being privileged to please God a little more in an abandoned shed.

"In the morning the communists chased us into the truck with great tumult. After about an hour of traveling, four of the Sisters were taken off, one of the communists leading them away somewhere. They kept dividing us frequently in groups, till finally only Anna and myself were left. We kept looking at each other when we were left with only one communist to guard us, as if to ask what would happen to us. Will we go together? Will they part us? When and where will it be?

"They did not part us that day. We were taken to a glass factory in Bohemia, directly to the establishment, where we were told to sweep the working quarters. Later, we toiled among the workers. They also gave us living quarters. I was placed with two women workers, and Sister Anna was quartered with a family.

"The atmosphere was bad—worse even than at the collective center. The people at the factory made fun of us, and the manager tried to make us give up our habits by pressure methods. In my quarters I was unable to pray openly in the presence of the working women. They laughed at me and made a racket when they saw that I was praying. Thereafter, I prayed only in silence, but all the more fervently.

"Anna had a hard time of it at the Czech household, for she was with a communist family. The master was some sort of a leader in a revolutionary workers' movement. In addition, he drank. He would come home late and raise a rumpus, both with the family and with Anna. He scolded outrageously—only as a person of low morals hating all that does not conform to his communist ideas is capable of doing.

"More than once have I seen Anna crying at her machine; and several times she secretly gave me slips of paper on which were written brief snatches of her bitter fate.

"I passed information about myself to her in the same way.

"At the factory it was a veritable hell. We were purposely placed among the most experienced communists. There wasn't an hour—nay, even a minute—when they weren't disturbing us. Once they would impose the hardest kind of labor on us; then again they would chase us to a new department and demand that we do our job in less time than senior workers. They controlled and inspected our work for

79

sabotage, and to see that everything was in order. If by chance, and on account of our ignorance of departmental work, we made a mistake, there was much shouting directed against the Church and Slovaks in general. So much blasphemy, rude insolence and hatred I've never before experienced. Neither have I ever heard of anyone capable of offending so outrageously. I am sorry and grieved for the people whose morals the communists had corrupted so deeply.

"Most loathsome were the talks, the obscenity of which was directly killing our souls. We were unable to close up our ears, for our hands had to work and our ears listen for new orders. We were unable to escape, for we were under strict supervision.

"We scolded these shameless people and entreated them. But this only made them all the more rude and offensive. I am now convinced that they had been trained expressly for this abominable role—to poison and press us still further into the ground.

"Prayer was our only solace and protection.

"Then came the tragedy: but it may even be considered salvation. One evening, when Sister Anna was already asleep at the communist home, the master came back drunk and made a clamor.

"He did not find his wife at home, and started calling all over the house. But the son and daughter were also away— perhaps at some communist place of amusement. The drunken communist cursed, smashed doors, and ran all through the house. Finally, he thought of Sister Anna. With a curse on his lips, he rushed into her room.

"Before Sister Anna was fully awake, he rushed at her bed and his hard fist fell directly upon her head. She just sighed a little. Maybe, in his unnatural state, the communist didn't even hear her. He asked about his wife and children. Anna tried to quiet him down as best she could, and told him to look over the house again or go to the neighbors.

"This was a salutary thought. The communist left the room, and Anna dressed quickly. She threw on the various parts of the habit, not unlike the mechanical preparation for

80

another working day or to go out to work on a new shift.

"And it was fortunate that she did so. For the Bolshevik soon came back, his mouth frothing from continual shouting and raving.

" 'There is no woman in the house, and I want a woman!' he cried out like a wild beast.

"Anna trembled as she prayed and moaned that God give her sufficient strength to get by this danger successfully. She had scarcely collected herself when the communist started running for her. Both his hands were upraised and aimed directly at Sister Anna's face. He probably wanted to close them over her mouth, to prevent an outcry.

"Anna stepped aside, tore down a picture that was hanging over the bed, and hit the communist in the face with it. Then she grabbed the bed covering and wrapped it around her enemy's head. He kicked and squirmed, but was drunk and could not use his strength. Anna also pulled off a bed sheet, tied it around the communist's feet, and fastened it together with a large pin, so that he was practically fettered. Then she got a piece of hemp, and with it bound up the ravisher's hands.

"But, actually, this was not at all easy. She had to wrestle with the communist for half an hour. She wrestled and prayed that not any of the family return before her task was done.

"And God *did* help her!"

"May He be praised and glorified!" said Dubovan.

"Both of us were fortunate. That night I had to start working on a night shift, and by chance both women workers with whom I had to live came home that week only after I had gone off to work. Properly speaking, we alternated. That evening there had been some ugly girl staying up with me, but she went home rather early. She said she had other duties to perform; for there would always be a visit when the women workers left. Once a supposed cousin would come in; at another time a godmother, or some other relative, or the friend. They might bring a message, or come to ask for something. And all this was to watch me so that I would not escape.

"But that evening they were not guarding me. Matters went along smoothly, as though we had planned them out that way. Anna rapped on the window of my room. I got up and looked out. She was hooded up in some kind of a sheet, for she didn't want to be recognized if anyone happened to meet her. When she saw that I was at the window, she uncovered her head; and I could clearly distinguish, even in the dark, that it was she.

"We quickly reached a conclusion, and I dressed up even more quickly. I picked up a working skirt, and grabbed up another one from a neighboring closet for Anna. We put them on and went out of town by side streets, hastening our steps.

"And this did save us to the extent that we got out of town, where we were less conspicuous. We considered our plans briefly and promised to meet each other in Slovakia. It took me a long time to come back, but I got here. The manager of this hospital doesn't know who I am, other than the fact that I am a religious person. Externally, I even took a new name. And I have news of Anna already. She came to Zemianska Huta, and now Father Pavol is trying to get her a job."

"You certainly are marvelous children," commented Dubovan.

"God helps us, and we will continue to look out for others as well as for ourselves. And I ask you to warn everyone with whom you come in contact, and whom you can trust, not to allow himself to be dragged into slave labor, especially outside of Slovakia."

Save Our Youth

DURING THE period of Slovakia's freedom, Dubovan's village had had a good teacher in Stach. He devoted himself to youth and built up organizations; he directed plays, had an excellent choir, and fostered love for God and country. The village respected him, and everyone was his friend.

But when the communists came, Stach was forced to leave the village. His pupils grieved for him, as did their parents. Before departing, Stach had talked things over with Dubovan far into the night—about what awaited the village, Slovakia, Europe and the whole world, unless it awakened in time to oppose Communism more energetically. Dubovan finally embraced Stach, shook hands with him, and looking him squarely in the eye, said: "Go your way as your conscience bids; but we will meet again, Teacher Stach. For you've etched out a profound impression on our hearts, and I know that you will come again. You are still young and healthy, and your spirit soars high. So work and fight persistently, and may God be with you!"

"And with you too, Dubovan! I will never forget you, and will return as soon as I am able to. The last ten years of my life here have made this village my home."

A tear seemed to glisten in Stach's eye when, slightly bowing his head, he parted with Dubovan.

Stach kept his word. He would come to see Dubovan on special occasions only, for he now lived quite a distance away from his former village. They were festive days, both for Dubovan and the village. Children crowded about their former teacher, and he had to sing and play with them and accompany them on hikes in the fields. Older pupils confided that they did not like their new teachers. Stach, in turn, admitted that he felt wretched in his new assignment, for there was not a single teacher there in whom he could confide.

But Stach was under constant surveillance and his visits became progressively less frequent, till finally they ceased altogether. Now only Dubovan would get an occasional letter from him, and even these epistles never gave his correct address or were signed by his right name. Dubovan knew why, for he was wide awake. After receiving his last letter, Dubovan was almost certain that Stach would see them again. He felt that Stach would be obliged to come and inform them about what was going on at the schools.

Stach did not disappoint Dubovan in his expectation; for he did come—but at night, and the meeting took place outdoors under the hills of Brehy. There he met Dubovan and two other respected citizens, friends of both Dubovan and himself. Stach had sent his mother to see Dubovan to arrange this meeting place. When darkness came, they would repair to a nearby shepherd's shed to spend the night—or rather, the vigil—if necessary. For by morning Stach had to be at another place; neither could the three respected citizens, especially Dubovan, afford to remain out of the village very long. Militia men had been on Dubovan's trail ever since the spy Cyril visited his place.

Stach's eyes glowed with fire. After an absence of seven years from the village, he seemed an entirely new person. It was only when he smiled and began to talk that Dubovan recognized in him the teacher Stach.

"You already know what happened to me. I was sent to the mines, for the regime did not consider me to be a reliable teacher. But I escaped and am continually on the go. Even this visit is but a short stop. I am sorry, and it touches my heart to the quick that I cannot greet the entire village, especially my former pupils; but it can't be helped. I can't afford to bring down evil on you, the village and our youth. I came but to tell you how the communists scheme against our youth, how they take them and poison them, and how they slander the Christian character of our people."

"Thank you for the visit, Stach," said Dubovan. "Now give us all the information we should have; and while you are doing so, take this and eat as if you were at your own table." Here he gave him a piece of homemade sausage, white bread and a cup of whiskey.

"Here's to our health!" said Stach as he lifted the cup.

"May God hear us!" responded the three farmers.

Stach talked as he ate, in order to conserve time. "I'm certain that this happened among you also. At the beginning of this school year, parents received a special questionnaire.

They were asked to check this questionnaire as to whether they wanted their children to attend religious instructions or not."

"Yes, we did get such a questionnaire. The school director himself delivered them to us in person. He got around to us before the beginning of September," one of his three friends interrupted Stach. "The director requested me to declare at once what I intended to do—whether I was for or against obligatory hours of religious instructions in school."

"You state the case correctly, friend. Directors were obliged to bring these messages to parents personally. Parents, in turn, had to testify in their own handwriting how they had decided, within that same day.

"The communist ministry of schools in Prague had two things in mind. First, it wanted to avoid unfavorable situations among the people. They gave parents less than twenty-four hours to decide this matter, to prevent them from getting advice and acting on agreement. Therefore, the director, or two or three of his representatives, scattered over the entire village and demanded all decisions on the spot.

"The communists' second idea was a purely personal one. The government was testing its school directors and their assistants as to their loyalty in the service of the Communist Party, and their cleverness in persuading parents from enrolling their children for religious classes."

"Out here all of us demanded religious instruction for children," chimed in Dubovan.

"At the villages of our inspectorate, approximately ninety-eight per cent of the parents did the same," said Stach. "Even in towns where conditions were different, the percentage of parents who did not want religious instructions for their children never exceeded fifteen. My director would either call parents in or would visit them individually. He had a definite time for everyone and would never allow two to meet about this affair at his office at the same time, especially not acquaintances, friends or relatives. Everything was figured out exactly.

"One of my friends, who only feigned to be on good terms

with the Communist Party, secretly allowed me to read the instructions from Prague; and there the directors were ordered to use all their powers of persuasion to convince parents that it was unnecessary to have their children instructed in 'religious obscurantism.'

"A personal accent in the directives was placed on Czech teachers in Slovakia that they should especially devote themselves to this matter; and, if help was needed, either to call for it or announce at once how it was necessary to advance against 'blind Slovaks,' so as to wean them away from priestly cassocks.

"Defeat of the Christian spirit in Slovakia meant then, as it means today, an exceptionally good sign of building up a 'Socialist Slovakia.'

"That's how it was stated in the secret directives, and that's the way it was acted upon. If a director or his representative did not find a father at home, he came back again about an hour or two later. If he was still not at home when he came back the second time, he would urge the mother that a very serious matter was under consideration, and that it would suffice if she alone signed the declaration."

"They played it the same way here," subjoined one of the three, who had been intently following Stach's account. "But the director sure did catch it from the women! Such hot-peppered soup he could have spared himself. They gave him an actual baptism of fire, and he found what he was looking for."

Stach took over again, saying: "Directors had no bed of roses anywhere. All the people were firm and unyielding.

"And as a matter of fact, they made absolutely no headway with farmers. But they had more means of persuasion at their disposal with laborers and officials. They ridiculed the idea of laborers considering themselves as pillars of the People's Democracy as long as they insisted on entrusting their children to priests; that it was foolish for them to consider themselves progressive, and yet have male and female religious persons instruct their children.

"Moreover, they insisted that the worker should be aware

86

of the fact that the Communist Party rewards its faithful followers. 'Why should you, Paľo, always be the last in the factory, when you can be a leader? Why should you, Ďuro, be dependent only on seasonal summer work with stone masons in the village, when you can work in the big city all year long and bring home a substantial saving? You can make enough for both yourself and family if you do more work than your quota calls for. Why, you can make even enough to go to the baths in summer!'

"Thus they insisted on confusing workers, considering them as their supporters and in their ranks, and relying on them to gain them most adherents; especially when, in addition to all the propaganda, they added the deception that the People's Democracy was but the government of the working class.

"In this connection a convenient chance came their way to assault the so-called 'bourgeois nationalists'—that is, Slovak communists who rode the Red horse even though they had doctorates of law."

"Are you referring to that Husák, Novomeský, Clementis, and the rest who were imprisoned and one of them already hung, Mr. Stach?"

"Yes, I refer to those. They pursued glory, but murdered and imprisoned people. But this lasted for a short time only. They reached the top and attained high positions. But their downfall was as rapid as their ascent, and they fell flat on their face. For Communism is such that it will not permit clever people to remain long in power. Moreover, these particular Slovaks were on the wrong track for not being pliable enough for Russians, neither were they willing to subordinate to Prague. They were smooth communists, but were unwilling to let outsiders order them around. But such outsiders *did* rule them, even giving them that fatal last order— to the gallows and to prison."

"They finished as they had lived," added Dubovan.

"For they deserved no better fate," resumed Stach. "Communists are afraid not only of conscientious Slovaks and natural leaders of Slovak towns and villages, but also of

87

their own members who dare to think otherwise than the Communist Party or its secret service.

"That's why they supervised school directors so strictly, to see that they carried out their directives. School directors, in turn, craftily turned this pressure on officials and highly educated citizens in the matter of religious instructions. Today the schools are almost entirely communized, as far as teaching current subjects is concerned. Russian is taught there, lectures given on the history of Communism, and every period must include references about Soviet greats and the Bolshevik army. They publish picture books where Stalin and local communist leaders are portrayed in place of God and parents. In a word, they poison our youth to the very depths of its soul.

"An example will best illustrate how they conducted the drive against parents and officials. I had a friend who was employed at a great state establishment. He was satisfied with his work, gave everyone his due, and thought that communists would let him alone. But they did take notice of him, and especially in this operation against teaching religion in common and high schools.

"This friend signed his petition that religion be taught in schools.

"The school director called him, and he arrived exactly at the appointed time. He first questioned the director concerning his reason for this action. Pretending innocence, the director said: 'There is nothing special about it. We simply want to know how many pupils we will have attending these religious instructions, and how many priests we will need for teaching them. For, as you know, sad to say, we haven't priests for all these classes.'

"But this answer did not satisfy my friend. On the contrary, it roused him to suspicion, and he started asking more questions, saying that there were plenty of priests. And if there were not enough secular priests to go around, religious persons could fill it to give these instructions.

"The director then approached his role as persuader from a different angle.

" 'Do not be angry with me that I am surprised when I hear you talk that way, for I know that you are highly educated and an intelligent person. That's why I fail to understand why *you* want your boy to take religious instructions.'

" 'If I were more highly educated I would perhaps seek my rights under the law even more energetically,' answered my friend. 'For true education must be in harmony with the laws of God. Whoever doesn't believe in God has gone astray and his education is of a doubtful value.'

" 'How can you say that?' countered the director. 'Our country has joined the bloc of the most progressive states. It is for this very reason that intellectuals are expected to serve as an example of ability in progress to the masses at large, rather than cause setbacks.'

" 'We have but one duty, Mr. Director: not to retard the people and not to strive to swerve them from their traditional Christian character.'

" 'That is *your* viewpoint. I would expect a genuine intellectual to be in the service of progress, one who considers religion as outmoded socially.'

"But these words the director uttered already somewhat angrily, as though he wanted to impress my friend that he did not intend to debate about it. For, as a general rule, one cannot get anywhere debating with communists.

"After a brief pause the director quieted down and again tried persuading my friend. But now he came out in the open, reproving him to be conscious of the fact that he was employed in an important establishment, one which worked for the state and the Communist Party; that he had a good position and came in daily contact with the most progressive kinds of workers.

" 'And don't you realize that you will find it at least unpleasant,' insisted the director, 'when workers will refuse to obey you and demand your removal on account of your different outlook on the world? For that in itself means that you are joining the enemies of the working class openly. You should reconsider your move very carefully.'

" 'I *am* well informed about it, Mr. Director. It is said that workers are progressive, and some did allow themselves to be incited. But such men are rather uninformed than progressive. For cursing, slander, pounding a table, or running about a factory with a machine gun in hand are not signs of progress. Rather, it means being backward. A majority of the workers is given wholly to the principles it has inherited from its religious ancestors, even though it nods here and there to the commands of the comrades. Such workers still fulfill their religious obligations; and a priest, a good teacher, or that 'backward' official, as you would term him, mean more to them than the whole Communist Party.'

" 'You are going too far,' answered the director. 'Do you realize that such talk uttered elsewhere could bring about your dismissal from employment at once? I just want to give you a confidential hint that you will have difficulties at the establishment if you continue to insist that your boy be given religious instruction. They may give you an inferior position, which would naturally mean less pay. And at school, also, we will view your child in a different light.'

"Such was the word-for-word content of the conversation between the school director and my friend. He was shaken by these threats, but did not lose his self-control and would not recall his signature. Instead, he insisted that his boy get religious instruction directly at school."

"Did this decision of your friend bring about any consequences?" ask Dubovan.

"It certainly did. In a month he received an order—'We want you to leave within an hour, for we need you no longer.'

"This meant discharge from employment, and he at once asked the business council to give him other work, even at less pay.

" 'We have no work for a laggard like you,' was their answer.

"He went out to the employment office; but could get nothing there, for they already had him classified. 'You can get work as a common laborer in Bratislava,' was their response to his inquiry as to whether they would give him any work at all.

"He said that he would consider the proposition. He went home and there found his wife crying. For, just a short time before he came, the mailman had brought in a notice that they had to move out of the house. They could, if they wished, make a protest against this decision; but it would avail them nothing. My friend knew what the score was. Quickly arriving at a decision, he returned to the employment office and accepted the work as a laborer in Bratislava. That's how they reclassify those who will not obey the Party —from high positions to labor. On the other hand, a blabbermouth who daily confessed what a good communist he was got my friend's position. For departmental experience did not enter into consideration."

"That is very sad," answered one of the farmers.

"But that is not all," added Stach. "There is a whole range of other precautions against parents and their children. While I was still teaching, I also had to promise that I would seek all kinds of information from children about their parents and relatives, in regard to strictly private matters.

"For example, I had to find out from each child whether his father had much work at the office, and whether he played cards. Who came to the family for visits and how often? What parents talked about with their guests? Whether a father listened to foreign broadcasts, in what language, at what time, and how often? Did he take down notes during the broadcast? Whether parents went to church, to confession and communion, and how often? Did they go on Sundays only, or also on weekdays? Did they say their grace before and after meals in common, morning and night prayers? What kind of prayers were said? Would the father come home late at night? How often? What kind of books or papers did the father or mother read? Would they go to the theater, or would they go to movies? What plays or pictures did they like? Would they praise or slander Soviet pictures? Would the mother use powder and paint, and did she like jewelry? What kind of pictures did they have at home? What kind of books? What food provisions were in their pantry?

91

Flour, lard, meat, sugar and other items? Further, who were the pupil's friends? Which students did he like, and which ones did he dislike? And why?

"And even other questions, which would turn a person's hair gray if he took them seriously."

"And did you report all that to higher authorities?" asked one of the farmers.

"I was supposed to, but never did report anything. Neither did I question the children. Not when even the director himself, or an inspector, came to supervise such questioning. They admonished me twice that I was neglecting my duty; the third time I got a lecture. The director called me up to his office and said: 'I know that you are not doing your duty, and that you are not in the service of socialism. I also know with whom you associate, and that you go not only to Sunday mass but also to communion. You scandalize your progressive colleagues and give the children a bad example by holding on to your unenlightened teachings. We warned you twice, but it did no good. We will give you a third warning. Comrade Inspector has decided that you must stop teaching. From this day on, you are no longer in the service of the ministry of schools.'

"I was staggered at the thought of leaving school, even though I had expected it. I don't know myself how I got home that day, looking neither to the right nor to the left. For I felt a painful wretchedness and thought that life outside of school would be unbearable.

"When I got home, there was a new surprise. Two militia men were already waiting for me. They ordered me to take some linen and come with them at once. We traveled for a day and a night by train. The two kept me under constant surveillance. On the second day, we arrived at the mines at Nováky.

"That part I already told you about, and will tell you the rest of it. But first, a few words about what communists intend to do with our schools.

"According to the decrees of the school ministry in Prague, and the directives of the commissar of Bratislava—who is obliged to obey the school ministry blindly—godless operations in schools must go on. Children are being morally poisoned in a variety of ways and means. They even use films. Teachers are expressly ordered to take children to the pictures on Sunday mornings. This is done purposely, and Monday-morning lessons consist of writing about these Sunday-morning pictures. Children must write about the contents of the picture and set forth the impression that it made on them.

"Parents are helpless here if they wish to avoid persecution. If a pupil does not go to these movies, the teacher asks why he was not there. Thus it happened to a child of one of my acquaintances. He did not attend the movies, for his parents had taken him to church. The next morning the teacher asked him: 'Why were you not at the movies?'

" 'Because I was with Dad at church.'

" 'Your dad took you to church, did he not?'

" 'Yes.'

" 'Where does your dad work?'

" 'At the glass factory.'

"Two weeks later my friend did *not* work at the glass factory any longer. They expelled him, in the same way they had expelled my first friend who had insisted on religious instructions.

"And so it goes on and on.

"Another way of tearing children away from parents is to arrange for all-day Sunday excursions to the country, or for a visit to some establishment. Older pupils are taken out for so-called 'Sunday brigades.' They have to work in fields, sweep in factories, chop wood, or at least observe how work is being done, so as to 'learn,' as they term it."

"They have started with excursions even here," said Dubovan. "But they have not yet ventured on other projects, and we have no movies here."

"It is worked out this way," continued Teacher Stach. "They first concentrate their greatest attention on cities, for there they have the greatest number of workers concentrated. They mix these in with the more respected citizens, and so

93

corrupt both children and adults. When they succeed in making place for them, they will also scatter them among the villagers. They will keep on increasing their adherents until they have them in every village.

"I came across their hints for teachers! These have long been ready, a whole five-year plan for youth education. You will find them nowhere in papers or journals; but teachers and professors well know what awaits them and the youth. They want to alienate children entirely away from parents; they want to make them into an unbelieving proletariat—a people without principles or morals, who will blindly obey only the Communist Party and fear the police. In other words, a people entirely subject to the regime.

"To accomplish this, they need their own teachers and professors. Therefore, they do not tolerate so-called 'burdensome' educators, capitalistic inspirers, and faithful Christians. They have expelled almost all of us. Progressively, they make this transfer either into industry or into prison.

"At the same time, they educate their own people. Communists are concerned about having good propagandists on their side. Therefore, they seduce capable newsmen and good actors. They even give consideration to people who understand technology and agriculture. Of course, even these must blindly fulfill the commands of the Communist Party. As a matter of fact, there are no establishments or undertakings where everything is not being directed from behind scenes by political commissars.

"But otherwise, they have no use for the intelligentsia. They make fun of it and educate their own usurpers. A typical example is the education of communist teachers. Communist-indoctrinated workers are sent away for special courses, return in a short time and are assigned to schools. At first they act as directors; but if this Calvary lasts very much longer, our schools will be manned exclusively by such hastily educated communist 'teachers,' who have had neither proper preparation nor the education for their calling. Some of them can scarcely sign their names."

"Nothing good is in store for us," added Dubovan.

"That's why I came back, my dear friends. I want to inform you of what is going on, and what, with united effort, we must do to counteract this evil and not permit our people to be ruined.

"To you I can reveal that I belong to a secret group of teachers which has taken upon itself to warn all Slovakia, even as I now warn you, against the terrible and destructive education that communists are preparing for our youth. But we, who have devoted ourselves to the task of education, and whom the communists have banished, do not flee from responsibility. Let happen what may, as long as there remain but ten of us free, we will go about towns and villages, even to the most remote corners of Slovakia, rescuing our youth."

"How do you plan to make this scheme work out in practice, friend Stach?" asked one of his three listeners.

"It will not be an easy undertaking; but with courage and good will, we can still save much. In every village we will need at least three men like you. We will have to organize secret schools. Let us say, right here where we sit, we can have fifteen children at one time, twenty at another. You can explain to them the most essential matters: one can lecture on religion, another can read them good Slovak verse, and the third can draw their attention to good books. And the three of you together can foster in them a spirit of anticommunism.

"That is the work waiting for you and your village friends, Mr. Dubovan. Even as your father, before World War I and under Hungarian domination, had passed out Slovak newspapers and books; just as he had gathered youth at spinning projects and other winter evening recreations, and informed them how they had persecuted Andrej Hlinka; how Ferko Skyčák, Ferdiš Juriga and Martin Kollár fought valiantly; what a great hero Svetozár Hurban Vajanský was—even so it is necessary to renew that tradition today. Today we can place worthy examples from Slovak history against Stalin, Gotwald, Zápotocký, and Siroký, and instill it into the heart of our youth that not Communism, but Christianity and democracy will save our Slovak people."

"That's the way we must go about it!" spoke up the three

upright farmers at once. "You can depend on us, Mr. Teacher."

"But I have to go now, dear friends," added Stach. "I go where I can make myself felt, for I want to repay Communism in full."

"May God help you and protect you," said Dubovan, gravely lifting his head. Out from Brehy a pleasant autumn breeze rustled through Dubovan's graying hair. Stach, stopping at an opposite hill, waved once more, and the peasants returned home—to the task of saving their youth.

Hosts Scattered Over Manure

DUBOVAN'S NEPHEW Ján arrived in threadbare civilian clothing one April afternoon, and in a terrified state. Mrs. Dubovan and the neighbors, old and young alike, were frightened when Ján related what had taken place in their monastery three days ago.

"Armed militia arrived at night," Ján began. "They invaded the monastery and the church at once and ordered all the fathers and fraters to get ready to travel. When Father Guardian protested, they answered: 'You rectory rascal, we are not interested in your talks! I have ordered you to get ready, and that suffices.' "

"But how were you to get ready?" interrupted Ján's aunt.

"That was but an empty phrase. They ordered us to assemble in the rectory and forbade us to take anything. No clothing, linen, or prayer books. All of us trembled. We anticipated that something was about to happen, for they had been jailing priests for months. But it was hard to visualize them coming to get all the monastery inhabitants at the same time!

"Father Guardian endeavored to soften the heart of the militia commander. He said that all the priests and fraters were innocent: that they performed only their religious obligations and payed no attention to politics.

" 'For that very reason, do not entreat,' the commander cut him off. 'If you are innocent, what have you to fear? You are supposed to have a strong ally in your Christ, your Pope, and in your American reactionaries. The heavens will overwhelm us peace-loving citizens and we will become a papal colony if we move but a hair on your head; atomic bombs will burn out the dwellings of the citizens if we take you away from here. Is it not so, fatted rector?'

"The monstrous eyes of the commander opened up even more, and a dirty smile played on his countenance—such a smile as is seen only on criminals and demented people.

"A chill ran up my spine, and I noticed that my confrères lowered their gaze. They would have dropped to the ground, had not the policeman roared on: 'I have orders and will carry them out! I have an opportunity and will follow it up! I have two fists and will use them! I have a mouth and will not remain silent!'

"Suiting actions to words, he had the fathers manacled, leaving us fraters standing beside them.

"When Father Guardian and the rest of the manacled fathers started reciting the rosary aloud, a policeman rushed at him and hit him so hard with his bearlike paw that the father staggered and fell on a nearby table. But the commander and his subordinates did not hesitate to drive him off the table. Two of them grabbed him by the arms while a third pulled out a blackjack and hit him three times over the back with it. At the third blow he stood up again. He raised his eyes, and to me it seemed that he prayed like Christ on the cross, 'Father, forgive them, for they know not what they do.'

"We prayed also, not aloud but in whispers, each one for himself. We prayed not that God would remove this tribulation from us, but that He would give us the courage to bear up under it—as Father Provincial had formerly instructed us in closed spiritual exercises, and as we had learned from reading the lives of saints and martyrs for Christ's truth. Prayer does help. Every one of us persevered, even though the beatings were repeated. They beat up every father in the group; but only threatened us fraters with blackjacks and manacles.

"Then they ordered the fathers out into the yard and ordered one of the fraters to harness the team.

"No one asked what was to follow, for questions would only invite further beatings and insults. But, notwithstanding, Father Guardian still dared to make a request—not for himself or the religious order, but for the holy state of the priesthood. He knew that there were sacred hosts in the church and the priests could use them. So he made his plea to the militia. He requested to be permitted to go to the church and asked for companions on this mission.

"This time the policeman did not reply with a whip, for a new idea struck him. His countenance held an involuntary smirk as he cast godless eyes toward his comrades and gave the order: 'You two stay here, while you five come with me to the church.' He took one of the fraters along to lead them through the hallway to the church.

"On the following day this frater had an opportunity to tell me briefly what had happened in the church. When they arrived at the church, the commander jumped on the altar, tore down the cross, spat on the statue of Saint Anthony, and started crashing the tabernacle. When he found that the door was made of steel, he ordered his comrade to break it off with a bayonet.

"During all this time he was making a clamor as though he were at a market place. His young comrade fulfilled the abominable order and tore out the door. At this the commander started whinnying like a dumb colt in a pasture field. He pulled out the monstrance and two chalices full of hosts. He handed the monstrance over to a comrade at once, remarking that it will come in handy 'for something.' But he held on to the chalices and, laughing diabolically, carried them through the church.

"He stopped in the center of the church and asked his comrades: 'Have you had your breakfast yet?'

" 'Yes, we've had our breakfast.'

" 'You might take a refection if this bread that papists prepare every morning does not turn your stomach. Taste it. It's supposed to be manna. Try it yourselves.'

"He took a fistful of hosts and started passing them out to the policemen. They wanted to take them into their hands, but he would not allow them to do so. 'You are supposed to receive them in the same way as the Roman serpents pass them out,' he said as he approached the lips of the nearest policeman with the hosts. The comrade seemed to open his mouth quite willingly; but the leader's eyes sparkled as he screamed in a highly pitched voice, 'Open up your mouth that I may feed you!'

"With this he shoved a handful of hosts into the policeman's mouth!

"The receiving comrade made as much of a mockery out of it as did the commander. Spitting out the hosts, and cursing in the choicest Russian idiom, he laughingly blasphemed God, saying, 'Candle-bearing women fold their hands when they receive but a crumb of this ordinary bread. So sweet, supposedly a blessing from some other world! But you gave me a whole fistful and still I feel nothing. Only dried-out fragments and crumbs. And yet rectors fool people with this folly, instead of teaching them to work and hold together where it will benefit them, and where discord is not sown over such foolishness.'

"This was hard for our frater to bear, but he withstood it. He was forced to, and thought that God Himself must have elected him to witness such unheard-of humiliation of His home and of the Son of God Himself.

"But this was not all. Intoxicated with vainglory, the Reds made clamorous outcries in the church and rushed out of it with a tumult. Their commander stopped at the door for a few moments, as if in reflection. Arriving at a decision, he gave the signal to proceed.

"He stopped the policemen in the hallway and burst into the refectory, where we were gathered, giving us the signal to follow him. In the hallway we saw the rest of them, one of them holding the two chalices that the commander had given him. The commander now asked the coarse question, 'Do you raise hogs?'

99

" 'Yes,' answered one of the brothers.

" 'Let me see the pens,' commanded the leader.

"I thought they were going to confiscate the hogs. But they had come to get us, and wanted to make it clear that they would humiliate us first, and only then confiscate monastic property.

"We followed the commander with heads alert. I noticed the strained faces of the fathers. They prayed, and I prayed along with them. We were not going to Golgotha or to a Calvary, only down the cloister hallway which at other times had resounded with religious chants and millions of prayers for benefactors, sinners, for the conversion of Russia, for union of the world under the banner of Christ—that there be one fold and one Shepherd.

"These memories came back to me as we followed in this unusual procession where manacles on the hands of the fathers took the place of beads, and where a policeman with an automatic headed the procession in place of the senior father. Reluctantly, I sighed and asked the Blessed Virgin and Saint Anthony to help me and all of us to carry the cross given us in resignation to God's holy will.

"But this was no time for meditation, and I can't even now collectively analyze all that had happened, for my mind is still in a daze."

Up to this point Ján's aunt had somehow managed to keep from crying, only sighing here and there and pressing a handkerchief to her cheeks in order not to give way to open weeping. She was already used to many incidents. She remembered the pilgrimage to Staré Hory, especially how she had faced a machine gun directly; how the soldiers had manacled Rector Strelák; and how they had blasphemed God in the presence of this great throng of pilgrims. And she had been expecting something to happen at any moment. Every member of their family had been living in expectation, for never had a day passed by without bringing rumors of some bestiality of the militia or other unknown pillagers, who would scourge a farmer in cold blood, or beat up a good saleslady on the way to the market place. They had no re-

100

gard for a priest, a teacher, a former notary or burgess.

But now the aunt could not control herself as Ján told of the heartrending events that had taken place in the church and the monastic hallway. She thought she would faint, that her heart would break, that she could not live through it.

The young frater in civilian clothes, however, was a man. He took her by the hand and told her, "Auntie, dear, do not cry over the living and fear not for the dead, for they will obtain for us a happy death."

"But this is too much, my child! Your mother, at least, is more fortunate up there. May God give her eternal glory!"

Ján continued with the narration, for Dubovan was curious and his whole peasant pride was aroused as he said: "We go to Purgatory alive, so let us proceed calmly. Speak up, Ján, that I may know all before they take me also; and I will appear before the judgment seat of Him to whom we are all indebted even in difficulties, that we are found worthy to tread the earth and raise our eyes to the azure-colored rainbow of the heavens."

Ján listened to his Uncle Dubovan, and each one of his words seemed to echo the teaching of Father Guardian at the monastery. He recalled being in the hallway, where he had seen Father Guardian in manacles as he prayed for his enemies. Now he interrupted this reflection and slowly recalled the unhappy situation in the monastic hallway.

"We dragged ourselves along as though we were but shadows. But even such shadows revealed a proof of innocence. That prayer-hallowed hallway was our witness—but a dumb witness, for it could not speak. And our self-appointed judges were blasphemers who needed no witnesses. They were not people of Slovakia, nor suited for a cloister. They were violators and messengers of Satan.

"The commander looked us over as though trying to comprehend what kind of an assembly was really before him. But his monstrous eyes did not scrutinize us long.

"He opened the doors and, poking an automatic into a frater's side, shouted: 'Where are those pens?'

"The frater but lowered his eyes as he had done while

praying at the altar that morning. Neither did he part his folded hands. Raising his right but a little, he pointed the way to the barns.

"We marched in a group, as though we were walking to the gallows. But it seemed to me that everyone had resigned himself. The older fathers were like ghosts. In my imagination their hoods seemed to change into golden halos and their manacled hands even gave me strength when my youthful blood began to stir up and my conscience protest that this could not be tolerated.

"But we could do nothing, and a policeman was at my side also. He watched me closely, and his eyes were on my countenance and my shaven head.

"Finally, we arrived at the barns, some several hundred feet away from the monastery. The commander stopped and ordered us to stand in single file facing the pen. Alongside this pen was a concrete enclosure containing a pile of manure.

"The policeman now started laughing. Grabbing the chalices from the comrade who stood beside him, he jumped to the side of the concrete enclosure and scattered the hosts with his right hand over the whole breadth of the manure pile, so that they made a white girdle.

"A heavy sweat broke out over my brow as though someone were strangling me. It seemed to me that I was choking, that I was going to die of humiliation and shame."

Ján's aunt cried. But Dubovan quieted her down, and Ján continued, even though his own eyes seemed to glisten with tears.

"'Look at your Christ, this is your Papacy,' the ugly commander roared at us. 'Do you see? Open up your eyes and take a good look, you rectory miscreants! Ha-ha-ha! If you do not see anything, how your Christ has been overshadowed and the time of His enchantments is past! Now I will perform a circus act and make a cross in your honor. A cross on hog manure!'

"With this he approached the left side of the concrete enclosure and actually started pouring the host crosswise, so that we could plainly see a cross.

" 'Glory to the cross of Christ!' solemnly cried out Father Guardian, and to me it seemed that he was intoning a solemn Gloria.

"The commander was unable to gather his wits before all of us answered in unison: 'Blessed be God! The cross is our salvation!'

"But now he was already rushing on Father Guardian, and the remaining soldiers took care of the fathers and fraters. Each one of us took a blow: some over the head, others over the back; here a kick, there a knock. I took a blood bath.

"But in spirit I prayed. I offered up my sighs for myself, for a happy hour of death.

"They led us back to the hallway, and there we had a real fight. For sacrilegiously they again struck the priests and their faithful servants, the brothers.

"The fight lasted a good five minutes. Here on my neck there are still traces of it."

And actually, there was a heavy wound on the neck of young Ján.

"Breed of Cain!" shouted Dubovan. And his wife threw herself into Ján's arms and gave vent to her great grief and emotion.

But Ján was a man. He took his aunt into his arms and said: "That was but a drop, a small part of what I deserved in proportion to how they beat up Father Guardian, how basely they treated the rest of the fathers, and how madly they rushed the senior frater for being somewhat awkward about handling the team of horses.

"The commander raved and beat up Father Guardian the most severely. His comrades also wanted to do their part as co-murderers of our people, opponents of holy faith and public scoffers of God's teaching.

"They delivered blow after blow, all laughed satanically, just like those who had scoffed at Christ when they crowned Him with thorns and buffeted Him."

"That is very, very much for us to bear," said his aunt, this time overcoming her tears and outcries.

"Not for us young ones, Aunt—but for the elder fathers,

fathers who had been worn out with work, in science and on the missions. I knew they expected that something was coming, but perhaps they did not even dream that there would be so much of this terror. They had never prepared us for anything like this. They would warn us in general that trials would come. They gave us lively illustrations of the incidents regarding the imprisoned bishops, prelates, several of our starvation-tortured elder priests at the Leopoldov, the Mučeníky, and other prisons and concentration camps. But somehow they had always hoped that the scourge of God would not continually increase.

"But it *did* happen. However, God is good even when He tries us. We've had it good for a long time. We did not understand suffering; we did not know the meaning of persecution.

"Dulce est pro patria mori, but it is sweeter to be a martyr for Christ and the church."

"Your mother should have been living, Ján. She would have rejoiced over you, even in this sorrowful situation. She wanted you to be a priest, but I see that you are worth as much as a good priest. May God bless you! May his hand guard you forever!"

These were sweet words of his aunt who, under the influence of Ján's manly talk, aroused herself. And she herself made the motion: "You are utterly exhausted. There is a swelling about your eyes, and your voice breaks here and there. You need refreshment. Relax, and I will prepare a supper for you. Oh, my joy, my son! Your uncle and myself have hopes only in you."

"I will not fail you. Christian fidelity extends to the grave. You have been a father and a mother to me. To whom else should I turn for comfort and consolation? I have gained a lot of strength during these years in the cloister, and the voice of Father Guardian will ever be a reminder to me: 'Brethren, sons, let us be united in these tribulations and carry our cross in resignation to God's will.' These were the last words we heard from him when a policeman once again struck him squarely in the face. He said no more, humbly bowing his head, and his right cheek glistened with a current of blood in place of a tear. Our martyred Father Guardian parted from us with dignity."

"Parted?" asked Dubovan. "And what did they do with the rest of you?"

"Let it go at that for the present," interrupted the aunt. "Ján is fatigued. Let him clean up. We will have time to hear more after supper."

"Yes, you will hear more after supper," Ján assured his aunt and Dubovan. "I will tell you all and hold no secrets from you, for we are blood relatives. Moreover, the storm is overtaking all of us, and we are all under the care of God's providence."

Frater Ján went to a pantry to uncover his wounds in the twilight, for he had offered them up for the martyr Father Guardian, and also for the blinded infidels and crazed militia rabble.

The shirt was hard to peel off. Frater Ján prayed the sorrowful mysteries of the rosary while he undressed and washed the upper part of his body. He finished the rosary and meditation in silence. He cried for joy that he could meditate privately, at least for a while, on all that had happened during the past trying days; and he wondered most of all what would happen to the religious fathers, and what the militia would do with the monastery.

It was pleasant to dream in Dubovan's chamber while his uncle was guarding the door, and the martyr Father Guardian was praying for his altar brethren and sons—the religious fraters in the concentration cloister of Pezinok.

A Secret Mission

Ján's AUNT roused him from his thoughts when she knocked on the chamber door. She was calling him for supper. It had been a long time since he had eaten such a tasty meal. Ján's delicacy, cheese dumpling, *halušky*, were not wanting. Finally, it was topped off with a good poppy roll, *štrúdla*.

Ján soon became a different person, and both his aunt and uncle noticed it. When he had finished the second helping of poppy roll, and they had concluded the supper with prayer, Ján resumed the tale of his own accord, for he was conscious of the obligation to tell his own relatives more about it.

"At the conclusion of the big fight, and after we had heard Father Guardian's parting words as the soldier cut through his cheek, all the fathers and two of the eldest fraters were ordered to get on a wagon which had been made ready by our senior brother at the command of the militia leader.

"It was hard for the manacled fathers to climb on the wagon. But the soldiers shoved them, shouted at them, and made fun of them with the coarsest of jokes about religion and religious orders. Expressions used by outcasts and the lowest classes of people, such as a person will not hear for years, and which certainly never before echoed at the cloister yard of the town X, now resounded from the stone walls of this ancient building and touched even the heights of the church belfry.

"We wanted to help our manacled fathers to mount the wagon, for it was hard for them to climb up; but the policeman shoved us aside. A policeman struck an elderly brother so hard that he fell to the ground. And when this brother fell under the wagon, the Bolshevik had no mercy on him but kicked him in the privates so hard that the brother writhed in agony for a long time afterwards.

"This incident scared the rest of us off. We made no further efforts to help the fathers. Finally, we felt so sorry for Father Guardian that the two youngest of us, as if we had planned it that way, jumped up and boosted Father Superior on the wagon. For he had been so weakened by beating that he could never have made it himself.

"But the policemen did not forget us. The brother with whom I had helped Father Guardian mount the wagon took his medicine. A soldier struck him so hard on the back with an automatic that he fell to the ground and fainted. He re-

106

gained consciousness only after the wagon had left. I had to carry him to the monastery."

"And did they leave you alone?" asked the aunt.

"I don't know whether they forgot about me, or were intimidated by the fainting of the brother, or were in too much of a hurry to bother about me; but they did leave me alone. They only wanted to get away as soon as possible. A policeman with trained automatic sat in front, another remained in charge of us at the cloister. The rest mounted, two to each motorcycle, and went off to town as soon as the wagon left the cloister yard."

"And what happened to you and the brothers?" asked Dubovan.

"I will explain that to you at once. The policeman in charge ordered us to look after the one who had been knocked out on the ground, saying that he was merely pretending. I took him on my shoulders and carried him to the cloister. The policeman then led us through the whole monastery, looking through every room and opening up all the chests. Then he ordered us to collect the clothing and the more valuable pieces of furniture into one cell.

"Taking a fancy to one cell, he said that he was going to stay there. Then he ordered us to cook him some dinner, carry it to 'his' room, and to cover the table.

"We walked about the monastery as though we were strangers there. We knew not what was going on, or what would follow. We scarcely dared to talk. It was only when we reached the kitchen, and heard no steps in the hallway, that we breathed a sigh of relief and started regaining some measure of composure, uttering a sentence or two here and there. The middle-aged brother who had been with the policemen in church was very much dejected spiritually.

"We cooked the supper that the policeman had ordered and, carrying it to the cell, handed it to him. He released us and told us condescendingly that we too might prepare something for our dinner. But he ordered that we should report to him at one o'clock.

"We cooked nothing for ourselves, only drank coffee, for it

was almost one o'clock. We reported to the soldier promptly, anxiously awaiting what would come next.

"But we had a surprise in store for us. The policeman did not greet us with his automatic. He left it against a case as he rested comfortably on a sofa and contentedly smoked a pipe. At last he greeted us: 'Welcome, youngsters!'

"This was a strange way for him to address us, and we stood like statues before him. And he was full of talk—but it was talk totally different from what we had heard in the cloister yard, in the hallway, and in the refectory two hours ago. He was changed, and seemed not to be wholly on the side of the communists. Or was this strategy? we asked each other as we left his presence."

"And what all did he say to you?" asked Ján's aunt.

"It was not much. He asked us the usual questions during the interrogation of new people—when were we born, where we went to school, who our parents were, where our relatives lived, in what occupations were they employed, to what political party did they belong before communists came to Slovakia. . . . But he was especially anxious to know whether we had priests and male or female religious persons in our families."

"And did you tell him the truth, Ján?" asked his aunt.

"That I did tell him, for I had no way of knowing whether he wasn't already acquainted with the fact that Father Pavol is my cousin and Sister Anna my aunt. Therefore, I told him who they were and gave him their names in full."

"In my opinion, you shouldn't have done that," protested his aunt.

"Maybe I shouldn't have, and maybe it was better that I did," answered Ján. "But that did happen, and at my first visit to the policeman—that first forced visit when he gave us a hearing but did not treat us too badly.

"He acted the same way that evening when we brought the supper to him. He detained us and gave us our orders as to future duties: 'You will all live together in the big cell,' he stated in a normal tone of voice. 'You will keep the monastery in order; but do not go to town, and don't worry about the outside world. You are still monks until we get further orders. Today I spoke over the phone to your provincial, and he informed me that he will make arrangements for you. Until that time I am the absolute master of this building, which, from this day forward, has become the property of the working people.

" 'One more item, young men: Do not worry much about the church. You are not priests; therefore, you have nothing to do with it. A regular rector will come here; then we shall see how matters will be arranged.'

" 'And what about our fathers?' I dared to ask.

" 'That is a matter that concerns neither of us, but depends entirely on the people, whom priests are supposed to serve differently from the way your rectors had been doing. And I wouldn't want to talk about it with you, for that affair is settled. They have no permission to return, and you had better keep your mouth closed if you don't want to get into more trouble than they did.'

"Dismissing the rest of us, he had an elder frater remain alone with him for at least two hours. The rest of us had already finished up our evening work, and were preparing to retire, when this frater returned.

" 'I have been placed in charge of you,' he told us. 'We will keep order according to new regulations. Therefore, I want you to pay close attention to what I tell you, in order that we may not be involved in any misunderstanding.'

"This seemed strange to me. I fixed my gaze intently on this frater, and to me it seemed that he winked at me with his left eyelid. Was this a signal that I would learn more?

"I did learn more. This brother took a bed neighboring mine. When we had prayed and laid ourselves down to rest, I could not go to sleep, so I got up and started walking around. I started out for the hallway, but did not get there, for our room was locked. It struck me at once that we were now prisoners.

109

"I returned to bed; then I noticed our 'commanding' brother lifting up his head and, with his right hand, trying in some way to reach for me.

" 'Why are you not sleeping?' he asked in a whisper.

" 'Because I cannot sleep. All that has taken place has disturbed me so very much.'

"The brother then listened for a while, to see whether any of the other brothers would not overhear our conversation. When he was assured that everything was quiet—that is, that they were sleeping—he got up out of his bed and, squatting beside mine, he started talking: 'I noticed doubts in your expression when I returned from my visit with the policeman, but I gave you a signal at once that I would tell you all. Don't expect a full explanation at this time. I only want to assure you that, for the time being, we have nothing to fear. You and I will be sent out on a mission. I already talked about it today when I was questioned whether I would be able to visit the Father Guardian.'

" 'What should you have to go to see him for?' I asked the brother.

" 'I myself do not yet know why. On principle, I did not refuse this request. For ultimately, it is our father and our order that are concerned.'

" 'What if this mission should involve something against our religious life?' I objected.

" 'I tell you, I do not know,' was the answer I received.

"It was dark, so that I could not scrutinize the brother's countenance, to see whether he was feigning.

" 'And you also will be needed,' was the brother's next statement.

" 'What for?'

" 'To go on a mission.'

" 'What kind?'

" 'Maybe the same kind that I have received. I do not know exactly. From one single talk, one cannot gather in all the details. Would you go to Father Pavol and your cousin in Zemianska Huta?'

" 'I do not know.'

110

" 'Even though you are not sure of yourself, consider matters the way I've considered them. But the both of us should go. In the meantime, do not mention a word of this to anyone. Good night!'

"It was easy enough to bid one not to mention a word of it to anyone; but what about one's conscience, intelligence, relatives, honor? With such thoughts, I returned to bed. But I could not sleep for a long time. It was only towards dawn that I snatched a little sleep, but that was not much.

"During that whole day these thoughts followed me around like a bad conscience, as a threat, as a reproach, as terrible question marks.

" 'You will not go!' I told myself after each such question. 'Better to perish here, or to drudge somewhere in an uranium mine, rather than betray the religious order and my own cousin. For what else would they want of me?'

"But other thoughts also occurred. I recalled the many talks given according to the rules governing our cloister. Father Guardian used to tell us that religion should be protected not only by loud opposition, not only in the press and the pulpit, but hopes must also be fostered in the catacombs, and help given those who are abandoned.

"And who knows, brother Ján, whether you are not called to enter a catacomb of your own peculiar kind? Maybe this mission will benefit you. Maybe you will learn many things which would have been hidden from you if you persisted in stubborn opposition and allowed yourself to be beaten and dragged off to some unknown place.

"I fought with myself, the frater in me fought with a newborn person who was to be sent to a place that was very important to the communists."

"And how did you figure it out, Ján?"

"As you see, here I am, Auntie, dear."

"Therefore, you have determined to see Pavol, a Catholic priest whom you know to be uncompromising, who already has had many altercations with the communists, and who is giving them no end of worry?"

"I will go to him, Auntie."

111

"But how could you? Why do you do this to us?"

"Have no fear, and permit me to tell you how I arrived at this decision. I thought very much about it; and when I finally reached a decision, I made it according to the best promptings of intellect and conscience.

"The brother who had been at the hearing with the communist policeman the first day received another summons the next morning. When he returned amongst us, he worked very little, overseeing our work and gazing on me in particular as though he wanted my answer—whether I would go.

"But I had to give my answer to the policeman directly. The brother called me out that afternoon, stating that we were supposed to go to the comrade for an important visit. I anticipated what was coming.

"Nor was I wrong. The policeman was much nicer to me than he had been the day before. Finally, he seated us and gave us cigarettes. At first, his talk touched on our work about the monastery. He asked us whether we were getting accustomed to the new life. He spoke as though he were one of us, rather than a communist. When he was convinced that we were not complaining, and missed only the church, he said: 'You will have it better yet. I will free you, only do what I bid you. You will go to the Guardian at the town Y; and *you* to your cousin in Zemianska Huta. Give them my message and bring me back their decisions.'

"The comrade told us what he wanted, and finally stated that, on our return, we would be allowed to remain in the monastery and pick out any work that we like to do best."

"And what was the policeman's request?" the aunt asked seriously.

"That, also, you will learn some day."

"When?" asked Ján's aunt.

"Let him alone; he has much on his heart," interrupted Dubovan. He took Ján's part, although he himself began doubting his constancy.

"You will learn everything at the right time. This is not an opportune moment for discussing it. This very night I have to board a train for Zemianska Huta, for in two or three days I have to return to the town X with my report. Much depends on my journey. Maybe Father Pavol's very life hangs by a hair; maybe Father Guardian will suffer also if the brother who talked me into making this mission and I do not reach them. That is—*if* we do not accomplish the mission which is, thus far, a secret."

"I don't want to suspect you, Ján, but I am distressed over your talk. It is not at all clear to me; and the more I think of it, the more mysterious your mission appears. A wounded body and related beatings, father bound in manacles—and here the commander frees you and that other frater as though nothing had happened! He even entrusted you with a secret mission! That is indeed a mystery."

"Rest assured, Auntie, that I want to do only what is best for you. I will help all my relatives, whoever will be in need of help. I will help at such times when you think that all is lost."

"Very well, son, but I will pray daily that God turn you back if you have made a mistake—or have, for even a moment, hesitated under the influence of the promises made by Reds."

Ján laughed good-naturedly, then embraced his aunt and uncle. He asked them to remain composed and to allow him to rest for several hours.

Father Pavol

WITH HEAVY heart, and tears in her eyes, Aunt Dubovan accompanied Ján out into the yard. "Is he still a frater?" she asked herself when he was already behind the garden and Dubovan was closing the vestibule door and urging his wife into the room.

"We must not arouse too much notice at night. The less people see of us, so much the less talk, and all the more safety for both Ján and ourselves."

So spoke Dubovan, and expressed himself with conviction,

as though he wanted to indicate that Ján was in constant danger. His wife did not respond; but blessing herself before a picture of the Blessed Virgin, she retired. She talked to herself as she pondered over all the pictures that Ján's talk had impressed on her. In those pictures she saw an unfinished tint—the artist had made a mistake; or was it a false artist? And he wanted to deceive a Dubovanka! But he did not succeed. She saw that the last picture Ján had portrayed was lacking in color, and she could not admit that she was satisfied with it. That void made her feel hurt; that picture frightened her. She placed her hands over her eyes and turned to the wall so as more easily to banish the dark thoughts that this repulsive picture aroused.

In the meantime a train was carrying Ján among hills and places which he had never seen before. It was Slovakia, but Ján had not traveled much. He had left for the cloister as a boy, and had remained there permanently. If it were now day, he could have admired the beauties of nature. As it was, it was a tedious journey—at least until the official inspection. It came off on schedule, as the soldier had told him it would. He was closely surveyed and his documents scrutinized. But when they noticed that his hands were hardened with work, and his clothing relatively threadbare, he was left alone.

Later Ján dozed off a little. When he awoke, it was almost morning. As a matter of fact, it was the bustle of laborers going to work that awakened him.

"Move over, brother, and make room for that beautiful Marishka," said a muscled worker by way of introduction.

The frater moved over closer to the window and made room. The young lady sat down. But a young worker started crowding in beside her, and Ján wanted to get up. Others stopped him, saying, "Many good people can crowd in together; and as you have not slept long, you need not tire yourself out."

This revived Ján thoroughly. Somehow, he could not fathom such talk.

From what he had read in papers and heard over the radio, he had formed a bad opinion of workers. Consciously, he thought all of them were on the side of the communists. Even now he was inclined to judge them by what he had gone through four days ago in the town X.

But he corrected himself in spirit and praised this people. And he thought they were like his own. For Dubovan's neighbors and the whole village were ever like one large family. They helped each other in a spirit of co-operation. The laborer did not envy the farmer, and the farmer did not lord it over the worker, as they were brethren in poverty; both making but enough to get by on, without being able to afford any luxury. There was no reason for envy among them. Therefore, it was in this sense that the workers of the Pohronie had told him that a lot of good people can crowd in together, even on a modest third-class train seat.

Talk, jokes, and laughter suited the people. They talked about current events, leaving politics out. Nevertheless, here and there jokes were cracked about the rascality of the over-lords. Such expressions always had reference to politics in Slovakia. And they laughed heartily when someone related how a straw boss in the factory wanted to expel two workers; but the latter stood their ground, and the boss did not win the preliminary.

This was mild opposition. But Ján, whom no one in this association could have recognized, felt that Slovak people could never be talked into going on some secret mission, in order to serve secret commanders and the unmerciful militia. "If these people talk so openly in your presence, Ján, how do they talk among themselves, where they have no one to suspect? And who knows—they may have been trying you out when they made a place for you on the train seat and talked so nicely to you!"

Such was Frater Ján's mental survey of the situation; and so engrossed was he in his contemplation that he forgot that he was but a station away from Zemianska Huta. One of the workers mentioned that his wife was going to do some marketing at the Huta, and this aroused him.

It did not take him long to find the rectory of his cousin, Father Pavol. The father embraced him and at once seated him in his office, where there was no visitor present.

"Whatever brought you here, Ján? You come at an unusual time and in strange attire."

"Do not wonder at it. We live in strange times and must accommodate ourselves to them."

"Surely, you did not leave the monastery?"

"As you see."

"Not voluntarily, I hope?"

"That is an important question, my dear Pavol."

"Tell me briefly what has happened, for I am curious to know. You may fill in the details after breakfast."

"I come as a messenger to you, dear cousin."

"What kind of a messenger?"

"I was sent out by the new management of the monastery."

"And who is that?"

"An altogether new people, who bound Father Guardian and the rest of the fathers and imprisoned us in the cloister."

"You must have been but a petty culprit, since they left you out so quickly and sent you straightway after me. If you have become a traitor, do not even bother dusting off your shoes or crossing through any more doors in this rectory, but turn and go back where you came from. I want you to understand that Father Pavol was twice imprisoned, but they couldn't break him down. When they tried to take him a third time, the whole village surrounded the rectory. Three cars full of militia arrived; but over three hundred parishioners, armed with hoes, axes and pitchforks, marched out to meet them. Just as many women armed with kitchen ware poured hot water over the communists. The men battered the cars and younger men surrounded the militia. The soldiers retreated in shame. Come here, and I will show you how we live today at the Hutianska rectory." Jerking Ján by the sleeve, he pulled aside the rug, and Ján saw a button beneath.

"I want you to understand, brother of mine, that if you really are such as you might turn out to be—that is, if you are a traitor—I will but step on this button; and before you can reach the walk outside, six powerful men will take you

116

into custody. In that case you will not return to the town X, or even to town police headquarters, but will go where my parishioners will see fit to place you. We have already exchanged seventeen parishioners, for such queers and weaklings as you seem to be. I do not say this to frighten you, nor do I boast that it will remain this way; but thus far we did not give in to the communists. My parishioners are united. All of us form a hard core of opposition, open and aboveground. They see it and know all about it, but have been able to accomplish nothing here. They might have resorted to stronger measures had they not feared the anger of the people, and were they not conscious of the fact that a spark from Huta would jump over to Lehota, from Lehota on to Vieska, and thence to Bratislava, even as such sparks do fly around. And the more oil they pour on, the more dangerous the resulting conflagration.

"You probably knew very little about such matters in the cloister. But out here in the open, even we priests have changed a little. Now tell me what brings you to your relative at the Hutianska rectory at this hour."

"It seems to me that you would wrong me if you continued in the way you started out," answered Ján daringly. "They indeed sent me here, but the question remains whether I will accomplish what they sent me out for. I had considerable difficulty with Aunt and Uncle at their home last night, for I could not tell them all, and maybe I did not express myself clearly enough; therefore, they thought as evil of me as you do. But I wanted my freedom first. I got it and am glad I'm here. Another religious confrère, whom they have sent to the town Y, has also saved himself.

"The soldier has promised me much in the name of the People's Democracy, in the name of workers' justice, in the name of the social order, and in the way of better working conditions that they will supposedly bring about in the monastery. He promised me freedom, and that I may get married; that I may become the director of our monastery and peacefully work at the National Institute of Tatra. And if I learn to obey well, they will honor me with a headquarters of my own, where it will be a pleasure for me to live and enjoy myself."

"You are beginning to talk too much. If you were not my cousin, I would have no pity for you," interrupted Father Pavol.

"I tell you the truth that I am not in their service. Believe me! Believe a cousin, believe a religious person who has shed his habit involuntarily, one who bears it hard that he has to come to see you here. But I am no agent and not your enemy. I swear to you by the blessed memory of my deceased mother that I come here with a good intention."

"I can readily verify that, Ján. But that you may not say that a priest in opposition to Communism and its inhuman regime has no heart, I will open to you a brotherly and priestly affection. Come to the kitchen with me. Remain here quietly and take breakfast, for I must yet say mass."

"I'd much rather go to church with you and receive holy communion."

"And will it not be a sacrilegious communion?"

"If you want to hear me, I will also go to confession."

"Forgive me for prying so deeply into your conscience, but I am a priest and a fighter. Come to church with me. If you have sinned, bow your head; and, returning by a shorter path, follow Christ, as the rule which you have made your own in the monastery bids you to. Betray not your vows, nor the church!"

"I am glad to learn that you have such a stout Dubovan heart, Pavol. Uncle talked to me the same way yesterday, and Aunt suspected and reprimanded me, because, for the sake of security, I could not reveal all. But I will tell it to you today, for I had come expressly to warn you about things which you are probably not aware of."

"Come quickly to the church, for the bells are already ringing. Step boldly beside me, and do not scrutinize the men who will precede us by about five paces. The same number will follow us when we leave the rectory."

At this Father Pavol reached out with his left foot for the spot on the rug where the push button was located. Three men stepped out into the hallway and quietly preceded them. The frater did not look around. It was not till he was in the church that he noticed six men sitting beside him. But before they sat down, his cousin whispered something to one of them.

It was pleasant for Frater Ján to kneel in church. After four days of absence he was at mass again, and this time at his cousin's mass. This was the second time he had seen him at the altar, the previous occasion being at his first mass. It was the beginning of an entirely new life for him. For Father Pavol was his cousin, and he had come to warn him about dangers that beset him and, at the same time, to get help from Father Pavol. And when this was accomplished, both his aunt and uncle would learn what had happened and what he had been unable to tell them yesterday.

Such were his thoughts when, after Sanctus, he prayed for the living. He prayed for Father Guardian who had been dragged off; he prayed for the frater who had gone to the town Y; and he prayed for his blood relations. He prayed also for himself that he would persevere in the understanding he had made with his confrère, when the latter had come to confide in him at night.

After communion Ján felt as though he were in a cloister. After mass Father Pavol knelt down and asked those present to pray for a special intention. Ján guessed what that intention might be. His cousin wanted to obtain sufficient strength to control himself, and not to harm Ján, but calmly to hear him out.

"But how could he wrong his own cousin that way?" protested Ján's voice of conscience. However, his inner voice may be correct. Father Pavol was a saintly but unrelenting man. Frater Ján also prayed aloud for his cousin's intention. And then he added an Our Father quietly for his own intention—that he tell Father Pavol the unvarnished truth and not leave him in uncertainty even for a moment.

The frater joined his cousin, and they went out of the church together. The guards again accompanied them to the rectory. But the rector stopped in front of the church, for

119

one of his parishioners cast his eyes on him and very reverently asked: "Have you a visit, Father Rector?"

"You well know that I always have visits. Here a relative, there a lord who but yesterday had lived in idleness. They all like me."

"Why, yes, but who is that young person? I haven't seen him before."

"And are you curious?"

"Not exactly, but I wondered whether he was a relative, or someone from headquarters."

"Have you come to church to pray, or to spy on Father Rector?" echoed a manly voice from the rear.

It was one of the guards who had accompanied them.

"Nothing of the kind, but surely I can ask a question."

"And I suppose you will carry on the message to that vagabond at the Dolný Koniec, so that he in turn may pass it on further, is it not so? We have been observing you for some time, how you carry on with him! But be careful, lest it blow you apart!"

"Reverend Rector, what kind of people are those who are about you?" asked the curious parishioner.

"Don't ask questions, for you must know them better than I do. You were born here; I have been here but for the past five years. But I know them, and from now on I will also take better notice of you."

"Just take it easy, for any pot is liable to boil over," said curious Michael Nález, as though he were threatening. He had been born in Huta, but no one knew where his father or mother were from. As a foundling, he had been cast about from place to place. And he tolerated it, valuing neither people nor money, for he was but a drunkard and associated with gypsies. When the Bolsheviks arrived, together with tattered Frolo he welcomed them to the Dolný Koniec. Frolo lived in a raw brick shack that his gypsy predecessors had built.

"It is useless to talk with that fellow. Let us proceed to the rectory," one of the rear guards addressed Father Pavol.

"It seems that they are wondering about me," Ján said

quietly to his cousin as he seized the knob of the rectory kitchen door.

"They trust no one; and no matter how much you promised to do what they asked you to do, they would still be at your heels—even as are the opponents. For they sent Nález out only to make a connection. There is someone also behind him.

"Now that you have been to communion, it will be easier to talk this matter over. We will eat our breakfast, then shut ourselves in my bedroom, where no one will be able to disturb us. I will make all arrangements with the guards, so that you will have nothing to worry about."

Even though the frater did not know how his cousin would treat him, still he felt safe, for any person possessing a good conscience feels secure.

He settled himself in Pavol's bedroom, where he was to complete the unfinished chapter and eliminate the last traces of Father Pavol's distrust.

"I will not force you, Ján. You will tell what you know, how you want to tell it. For a priest forces no one."

"Nor will that be necessary, Pavol. I will be frank with you and tell you all, as to one's own relative and a priest. Just as if I were making a confession.

"When I went with the frater to see the soldier, I got the commission to hunt you up at once and propose to you the plan of the militia and their church management authority. By the same commission, I am supposed to bring them back your answer.

"I made excuses as best I could. When nothing else availed, I said that perhaps I was not fit for such a role. 'But you were capable of protecting Guardian, and are willing to lay around here,' the soldier said. Finally, I consented."

"I know what that request of theirs might be," interrupted Father Pavol.

"Actually, that is not hard to guess, since they have bothered you so many times and consider you to be their worst enemy. But still, you will be curious about the contents of my mission.

" 'You are aware of the fact,' said the soldier, 'that getting your cousin on our side would mean much to us. We are not concerned about imprisoning him or persecuting him. We know that he is esteemed by all, and has turned the heads even of the neighboring communities. But we have something else in line for him. We want to prove to him that we are neither against him nor against the church. Rather, we want to reward him. We will be glad to promote him. If that will be necessary, he may choose whatever he wants—he may be a canon, even a vicar general. And we will place him into any diocese. Even as Dechet went from his diocese to that of Banská Bystrica, so Dubovan can go to Nitra, Rožňava, or anywhere else. Just as he will want it.'

"In other words, they would want to make you a priest devoted to the regime, or, more directly, a manager of a bishopric."

Father Pavol laughed. Letting down his right hand, he scrutinized his cousin. "And what else did they bid you to tell me?"

"That was all. They want an answer, and it was for that reason they sent me out after you. My confrère, who persuaded me to make this journey, has a similar mission to fulfill at the town Y."

"And are you not afraid that your comrade in town Y will betray you?"

"I do not doubt his loyalty for a second."

"Therefore, you are really sure of yourself?"

"I think, my dear Pavol, that an explanation is called for in this connection, for you are well acquainted with human psychology. I know that you can see through me and that you feel that I have something more to add.

"Still, I have placed the question before you. Now I will give a short account of what took place. Before the two of us reported to the soldier, this frater ordered me to peel potatoes. 'And,' he added, 'in order that it may be done more quickly, I will accompany you to the cellar and help you.'

"I had doubts concerning this frater. Therefore, as soon as we were alone in the cellar, I brought up the matter of our

122

coming visit and proposed commission by the soldier, which the frater had mentioned the previous evening. 'I see that you are afraid,' he said. 'That is proper, for you fear not people, but the voice of conscience warning you not to betray, but to remain true to your vows of chastity, poverty and obedience. I fully honor, maintain and will ever keep these vows, even as you do, Ján. I ask you to be one with me, just as our good martyr Father Guardian bade us to be. Let us be united for church and religion and see to it, in addition, that we save as many people as possible for heaven, for our Slovak nation, and its Christian traditions. It is precisely because we are called upon to accomplish this objective that it is necessary for us to get out of here, not manacled like the fathers, but free as the birds of the air. Here we are half-prisoners. The soldier lords it over our lives and freedom. We are still young. Life and people in the outside world need us.'

"I listened to the frater with open-mouthed astonishment and stopped peeling potatoes. The knife fell out of my hands, but he continued: 'Philosophy here will avail us nothing. A white lie in this case is a lesser evil. Therefore, I say to you that we will carry out this soldier's request and set out on our respective journeys. I know that you will have a choice different from mine. But we will get out. And the more we promise, the more confidence he will have, and our chances for escape will be that much better. It will all depend on our cleverness as to whether we save ourselves and do good out there in towns and villages, especially in the deep forests. Out there somewhere on the Magura, the Tatry, the Beskydy and the Polana. Frater Ján, this is altogether a new life. Let us set out on this new journey circumspectly but courageously. Say little where carelessness or words uttered even in good faith may expose one to an open charge of spying. Never cross a bridge, till you get to it! Frater Ján, will you make this journey?'

"Without hesitation, I answered that I would.

" 'Frater Ján, will you take another vow?'

" 'For a good cause, willingly.'

123

" 'We made our religious vows and will keep them, for we agreed just awhile ago that we would not betray them or violate them in the least. And now, with all respect to the vows and regulations which we have made and bound ourselves to keep, I modestly add a motion that we take another vow, which is as follows: With full responsibility before God and the world, I promise that I will never betray my sacred faith, that I will not refuse obedience to the church, and in times of Christian persecution I will do all I can to save souls and help as great a number as possible of clergy and laity devoted to God, the church and the people. Brother Ján, are you willing to take this fourth vow?'

" 'I am willing.'

" 'Even under my direction?'

" 'Under anyone's direction.'

" 'Then stand up, place one hand over your heart, raise the other and take the oath.'

"I did as the frater told me to, and when I made this vow I added, 'So help me God!'

"Then the frater asked me to recite this same vow to him, and he repeated it after me. This completed, we looked into each other's eyes and cried for joy.

" 'Now everything is in order,' I said. 'I will go with you and carry out the mission.' "

Father Pavol jumped up from the lounge and, embracing his cousin, asked him to forgive him if he had wronged him.

"You did what was right! Every intelligent person in your position would have done likewise. My Janko, we will help each other! We are young and our conscience is clear. With good people, we can accomplish much for our Slovak mothers, fathers, the Church, the persecuted and the imprisoned."

First Wave of Arrests

FATHER PAVOL wanted to compensate his cousin for having greeted him so suspiciously. He decided to tell him something of his own experience that afternoon. He also wanted to give frater Ján a better idea of current events, for in the cloister the latter had not had an opportunity to learn of politics in Slovakia.

"As you know, communists had me imprisoned twice," began the administrator Pavol Dubovan. "It was in the year of 1945, when any insignificant pretext sufficed to bring in an accusation against a person. Many had been dragged off to Siberia, and some of our best people hauled out before the communist courts, after which mock trial they would be either shot or hanged. All this happened to them because they protected their faith and upheld their nation in publically opposing Communism.

"Communists also came to get me. True it is that I refused to give them rectory equipment; for they came in as if they owned the place and demanded my typewriter. I asked them whether they wanted a loan of it. 'Return it!' they responded. 'That typewriter belongs to the people and we now represent that people.'

" 'But the people bought that typewriter for me,' I told them.

"Thus the angered communist hounds had no luck with me, and I chased them out of the rectory. But next morning armed militia replaced them and I was taken to Bratislava. They did not trouble me on the way over. But at the Bratislava police prison they beat me up, even as they beat up whole hosts of other people—priests, politicians, ordinary lady market vendors, hill farmers who would not give up their crops, subordinate officers who would not tell where their chiefs were, and upright editors who wrote openly about Bolshevik bestiality in Russia and about opposition movements of Ukrainians, Poles, and Roumanians. Some of these I knew personally, others were strangers to me. But suffering, beatings, and constant hearings quickly made friends of us all.

"The police who summoned me did not speak good Slovak or Russian, mixing in a lot of Czech with it. They beat me up six times. They beat me up so severely that they took away all my appetite for eating, let alone talking. Once I had to disrobe entirely. They threw me face down on a bench and struck me over the hind parts, and also the most tender parts of my body about the kidney region, with a stout thong. I still have marks from those beatings, and my kidneys will probably never heal.

"And there were cases where they injured others much more than that. For example, one student became deaf in both ears from these beatings, another lost fourteen teeth. A 'prisoner' has permanent hot iron marks on his back and on the soles of his feet.

"It was a shocking picture to see these upright people walking through the yard. One would be lame, another could not stand daylight and had to shield his eyes constantly from exposure to the powerful reflectors at night. There were 'prisoners' whose faces were black and blue. And did they allow them out in the yard? They did while I was there. But later it was said that they imprisoned some of the inspectors and released them from work, accusing them of intermingling. This was a supposed sabotage of the People's Democracy. It was a pity that someone was not able to get snapshots of such Slovak sufferers. Such pictures would have served as most eloquent documents. But not all of us perished, and those of us who went through this torture treatment will always testify to the truth. That's why I am telling you this, so that such matters may not remain hidden, but be passed on to the outside world."

"I have heard that during those times they not only imprisoned politically active agitators but also church dignitaries," said Ján.

"That is true. Out there they held two of our bishops— Ján Vojtaššák and Michal Buzalka—and did not treat them at all decently. This, in fact, was the first sign that the communists were going to be ruthless. Bishop Vojtaššák, as you know, was the first Slovak bishop who refused to take the oath of allegiance to the pro-Communist regime in 1945. Our Slovak people will ever remember him for that. He thus became the symbol of anti-Communist opposition, and the

126

people greeted him most cordially when he was returned from the prison, where they could prove nothing against him. They only took a part of his life; but later they imprisoned him again, and this time they gave him a twenty-four-year sentence, while they imprisoned the other bishops for life. Other prelates were also given very severe sentences. They strike the shepherds, thinking that the people will scatter and give in to them. But thank God, this is not so! For the more they strike us, the stronger do we become! It would encourage and strengthen you a lot to know my parish more intimately. Our citizens of Huta and our hillside farmers are a beautiful example of spirited resistance. As I told you this morning, outside of that Nález and his gypsy comrade, they are all united against the militia.

"But I have digressed, for I wanted to tell you something of my prison experiences. I will confine myself to two very important incidents. There will be time to tell of others later on. For we can't afford to stay until evening conversing here."

"Have you any special program for this evening?"

"I do not yet know definitely, for out here a person can't make plans. Only communists have plans. Our counterplans must be made from hour to hour, according to reports as they come in, or whatever a person is able to feel out. I tell you, it's a dog's life!

"In the beginning I was alone in a Bratislava prison cell. But I offered up my loneliness for my spiritual welfare and for those who suffered more than I—for those who had to take more severe beatings, and for some others here and there who had fallen and were ready to give in to the communists.

"Later on I received a companion. They shoved him in one evening. He had on the same kind of prison clothing. He was stooped and white-haired, but in his face I at once noticed dignity. It seemed to me that he was someone whom I had seen a long time ago. He spoke, but his voice was broken and I did not recognize him. Finally, we introduced ourselves.

127

" 'I am Rector Dubovan from Zemianska Huta.'

" 'I am Rector Olšovský.'

" 'My Lord Prelate Olšovský?' I asked, very much frightened over the revelation.

" 'The same.'

"His words, and the fact that I had to ask who he was, when I was well acquainted with the man, sent chills through me. They had crippled him beyond recognition. And he was a prelate who would sacrifice his very heart for the common man, one who was widely known as a humanitarian, a holy and a just priest. He was an angel in human form. That's how we as priests knew him, that's how his parishioners venerated him—so much so that he was noticed for it even in the press. Wherever he appeared, people would greet him with banners. That's why he traveled so little among them. He did not seek the glory of this world. And this, in turn, aroused even greater respect for him."

"Why was he imprisoned?" asked the frater.

"You will hear that directly. Prelate Olšovský became very friendly with me. He spoke little about himself, more about others.

"He gave me a lively description of the coming of the war to his own parish; and once he went so far in his talk that we came to the shooting of innocent people. It was in September of 1944, when Soviets flooded central and eastern Slovakia with their parachutes, killing not only priests but also civilians, and then had the nerve to call it the 'people's uprising!'

"Such an 'uprising' struck also the town where Olšovský was prelate. There, too, was an invasion of wild partisans with machine guns and followed by loose women. And at once they began molesting peace-loving citizens. It is not known whether the party mentioned in this particular incident was marked out for them, or whether they came upon it by chance; at any rate, the party concerned paid a very heavy penalty. This old farmer, with his wife and three children, was known as a good citizen and an exemplary Christian.

"Two armed partisans invaded his home and asked him to

lead them to the closest forest, where Germans, supposedly, were in hiding. The old man hesitated, saying that he knew of no Germans, that he had not seen them; that it was indeed hard to get any information about them; and that he had no information about the matter whatsoever.

"One of the partisans pressed an automatic to his forehead; but he did not flinch. Pride sustained the old man, and the partisan did not shoot, for his comrade mumbled something to him in Russian.

"The ugly invader withdrew from the old man, telling him to think it over till the following night. But on the morrow he must certainly lead them to that forest.

"The partisans came again the next day. The farmer was home with his whole family, even though his wife had urged him to go away. He gathered his family about him at the table and started leading the rosary. They were at the third decade when the partisans invaded again.

"As the middle girl, who had miraculously escaped from the catastrophe, later told it to Olšovský, they did not even close the door behind them. At the door one of the partisans roared at the farmer: 'Stand up, awkward farmer and German spy!'

" 'For God's sake!' screamed the farmer's wife, grasping him by the right hand to make him get up. But he made no move, kneeling there and continuing to pray aloud. The children started crying, and the wife ran about the room as though deprived of reason.

" 'Not another word out of you, you Roman hypocrite!' shouted the partisan.

"But the farmer either did not hear, or would not hear. He raised his voice and just as he said, '. . . pray for us sinners, now and at the hour of our death,' a volley of shots burst forth. A belt load of shells was sprayed out, striking the old man, his children and wife, all of them weltering in their own blood. The partisans then smashed the lamp and left.

"Neighbors heard the gunfire. When the first neighbor woman ran into the yard, the partisans were just leaving the home on which they had revenged themselves and perpetrated an outrageous crime.

"The neighbor stopped till the two wicked men passed by. When they had gone a safe distance, she entered the home of this simple peasant, where only dead bodies greeted her. But she still heard groans and the muffled cry of a child.

"She ran out into the yard, and from thence on to the third neighbor, where she roused her brother-in-law to get a priest, while she herself went for a doctor.

"'I arrived at the home of this fearful tragedy before the doctor came,' Prelate Olšovský told me. 'By lantern light I beheld a horrible picture. The bodies of the farmer and the two children beside him were cut almost in half. They showed no signs of life. The wife was covered with blood, but it seemed to me that she still breathed. One girl cried; but it was a horrible, muffled cry. She had been wounded in the foot. I gave them extreme unction, and was praying for their happy death, when the doctor came. He took charge of the girl and the mother, ordering neighbors to place both on a wagon and take them to a hospital. I also boarded this wagon, for the physician gave the mother very little hope. And she did pass away in less than five minutes. The girl was taken to a hospital and was saved.'

"It was supposedly an act of mercy that Prelate Olšovský was only imprisoned, but he endured other sufferings. Sufferings, did I say? Only the prelate, in his great modesty, called them that. It was something unheard of, which could originate in the minds of only the most heartless creatures."

Urged on by great curiosity, the frater asked: "And what was it?"

"As Prelate Olšovský told it, there came to his rectory new 'masters,' who roughly accosted him: 'So you are that evil German hireling, servant of reaction and American capitalism! You did not go away, but had the nerve to remain here? I suppose you want to continue inciting the people to rebellion and driving them to slaughter!'

"The prelate did not understand. For he had never engaged in political activity and had never anything to do with matters which could be considered as incitement to rebellion. Therefore, he answered calmly: 'I do not understand what you are talking about, sirs.'

" 'I'll remind you of it at once!' shouted the rude, unshaven stranger, who had torn into his office without so much as a greeting. 'Do you not remember that farmer, who refused obedience last year?'

" 'I recall a farmer who was shot, together with his children and wife.'

" 'And you went to help that traitor!'

" 'That I do not know.'

" 'What were you doing in the home of that farmer—trying to revive him and helping his wife and daughter to escape?'

" 'I did but my priestly duty. Preparing the dying for eternity is one of the priest's greatest responsibilities.'

" 'Don't change the subject! How can you help one who no longer breathes? You were in league with him; you had been giving him instructions. He acted according to your directions, for you were all to him. That's why he perished.' "

"That was blasphemy unto God!" said Ján.

"Such was the language of the criminals who swarmed into Slovakia at the end of 1944 and the beginning of 1945. And as you shall see, that was not all there was to it. They did not waste much time with Prelate Olšovský. A soldier grabbed him by the arm and rudely shoved him out of his own rectory.

" 'You are coming along with us! For you surely must remember where you buried that evil spirit of a farmer. We want you to show us that place. But better still, take a shovel as you come along.'

"Prelate Olšovský walked between the two soldiers, with a shovel on his back, through a town which he had served for many years and where he had been treated with veneration. Olšovský's parishioners shrieked with grief and consternation when they saw him; but the soldiers forced the prelate to take the shortest road to the cemetery. Consequently, before the people could regain their wits and organize, the prelate was already digging at the grave."

"What was he doing?" asked Ján.

"He was digging—for he was forced to open up the grave of the farmer who had been shot. They forced him to open up the coffins of the farmer, his wife, and two children. And when he opened them, they asked him the following: 'You loved them so much that you betrayed them into the enemy's service, so that they had to pay for it with their lives. Now, don't you want to honor them just once more? Declare yourself!'

" 'I do not understand. I buried them in a Christian manner, and now I entreat you to leave their graves undisturbed.'

" 'Entreat for this!' said the Bolshevik as he hit the old prelate over the head so that he almost fell to the ground. 'You will do what I, the representative of the people, order you to do. And do it at once! Do it just as fast as you were hurrying on to that farmer's home, scheming against the rising justice of this country. Act, rector!'

" 'What is it that you want me to do?'

" 'Bend down, even as you had bent down over them in their own room. Bend down and kiss your loved ones. For you Roman servants love to embrace each other at the altar. Therefore, kiss your wards! They are dear to you in life; now show us how much you love them. For you announce in church every Sunday that the dead should be remembered and helped. Here is your opportunity to practice what you preach. Help them; or at least here, before witnesses, prove how much you loved them.'

" 'It is their immortal souls that I love.'

" 'Where are these souls? Here we see but four bodies. And does this sight displease you? Oh, I guess it wouldn't please you. I suppose you would rather see here a pile of twenty peace-loving fighters. Is it not so?'

" 'I am no friend of violence and murder.'

" 'We are going to carry on no philosophical discussion, comrade rector. We must act, for we still have many obligations before sundown. You must obey this order at once. Kneel down and do it.'

" 'I will do as you say—but not willingly. I do it only to prevent greater difficulties.'

"Prelate Olšovský then bent down over the four bodies and kissed them.

" 'Believe me, it was not hard for me to do so,' the prelate told me. 'God Himself must have withdrawn from me at that moment all sensitivity. There was a little smell, but I overcame it.' "

"And what happened to the prelate afterwards?"

"They did not take him back to the rectory. Just at that time, a group of parishioners were nearing the cemetery when ten soldiers jumped from behind the cemetery shed and started shooting into the air. In the meantime, two soliders took charge of Prelate Olšovský and led him behind the garden to a road which led to the nearest town having a station for state police. There he was tortured for two days without food or drink. The prelate did not tell me much about this treatment. He does not like to talk about his own suffering. Even in this he is great. After two days they took Olšovský to the prison at the Bratislava police headquarters."

"Why to the police?" asked the frater.

"That was just the situation. In 1945 and later years, communists had complete control of the police. In judgeships, for about two years, here and there a more decent judge would maintain himself and hinder the greatest brutality and inhumanity. But at police headquarters, communists did as they pleased. Generally, everyone who was brought before them was beaten up, tortured and drugged with medicines. Then they would place before him a prepared statement, in which he 'admitted' everything the communists wanted to have against him, together with additional damning material against a host of other persons.

"Prelate Olšovský went through the same procedure. They beat him up and he was frequently knocked unconscious. But somehow he always had enough reserve strength and did not sign such a prepared statement. This angered the communists still more and they beat him up again.

"But in due course they had need of political influence,

especially when they knew that elections were approaching. Such an opportunity came in Prelate Olšovský's case. They stopped torturing some of the prisoners, even setting them free. Among them was also Prelate Olšovský. Thus he got into my cell, where he was left alone till his wounds healed. Then they sent him back to the rectory."

Father Pavol had scarcely finished this sentence when a small bell sounded somewhere under the night lamp. Father Pavol knew what it was. He stood up at once and told Ján: "That was an alarm, but have no fear. Come, I will lead you to a place where very few have ever been."

At this Father Pavol wiggled something and the whole wall, as it were, folded into half of the bedroom. He pushed Ján in and followed him. When they were on the other side, he shoved the wall back and secured it with three hasps, so that the men were thoroughly concealed. It was a decent room, rather a library, for around two of the walls were shelves of books.

"I enclosed the original library with movable wall-length doors when they started tracking me. It is insurance, in case the guards should be surprised, or if there are not enough men at the rectory. Here we will continue our conversation peacefully after we wait for a little while. Listen closely whether you hear any footsteps in the hallway."

Both Ján and Father Pavol heard them, and it seemed that someone had started pounding on the door; but they couldn't tell distinctly, for the rectory walls were made of stone. The rectory itself had been built over six hundred years ago, when Huta was founded. It was almost as strong as a fortress. There was no need for much repair, only a little adaptation here and there. Therefore, it had been easy to change the library into a secret hiding place.

"How long will we remain here, dear Pavol?"

"We will get a signal. In the meantime we can be perfectly at ease. As you see, there are no windows in this library; therefore, no one will either hear or see us. Now I will conclude what I was going to tell you about my imprisonment. Not about myself, but about a case which actually calls to heaven for just punishment of the culprits.

"One day we heard that in the fourth cell from ours—it was a single cell—the guards had found the young inmate hanged. He had been brought into prison a short time before, for reasons we did not know.

"He could not stand the beating and the police-managed atmosphere. Therefore, he committed suicide. He hanged himself. So was the rumor. Even as the whole communist system is a denial of logic, reason and good laws, so here too, the clumsy administrators of the police management put out the report that the prisoner had hanged himself. But in this case, they said there was nothing missing from his two-piece prison suit. And as I myself had twice experienced, before communists place a person into a cell he has to disrobe entirely; for they want to be sure that he does not take anything into the cell with him. Even when he is naked, they examine a person in such a way that they bore in a place where no decent person would ever place his fingers. They have a man wearing rubber gloves who fidgets there for a good minute.

"Now tell me, how could that person have hanged himself? They themselves hanged him; and in order to cover up their crime, they put out the report that the prisoner had hanged himself! I had no peace of mind about it; and when I was released from the police management, I looked up the relatives of that hanged person. I found his mother. She told me that her son was a very pious lad, and she ruled out suicide.

"But we must learn what is going on outside," said Father Pavol, interrupting his prison experiences. He was already leading the frater up the stairs which led to the attic. Father Pavol unclasped the hasp on the ceiling and pushed up a small door. They had free access to the attic. Father Pavol went out to the roof and deliberately removed one of the slates. From this opening they had a view of what was going on in front of the rectory.

Nothing in particular, for no one could be seen. But they alternated in watching—first Father Pavol, then Ján. It was not long before three soldiers came into view from around a corner. One of them gesticulated with his hands and nervously looked about the rectory. Finally, for no apparent reason, he motioned with his right hand for his comrades to follow him. In a short time they disappeared in the village.

Father Pavol and Ján went back down into the library. "Let's pray at least an Our Father in thanksgiving," spoke up Father Pavol.

They did so. They were but halfway through when a bell sounded. But they did not permit the sound to interrupt them. By the time they finished, the bell sounded a second time.

"We will wait for a third signal. For it is only when they ring the third time that we learn that we are in the clear."

"You have a fine organization here," said the frater to his cousin when they returned to the bedroom, looking at the secret door which closed into the wall.

"This is but a small part of our organization. And I am happy to tell you that thus far everything has worked fine. It is all connected with the people. As you see, they are united. The soldiers saw no one; and outside of the cook, they spoke to no one. There was 'nobody home.' Neither I, nor the chaplain. For he also has a similar hiding place. And our guards direct everything from their secret quarters. Moreover, they are all well armed."

"Yes, I notice that you have two automatics, even in this library."

"Absolutely: here we play for keeps. For we can't oppose heavily armed soldiers with bare fists, as had been the case at the outset. These automatics are reserves for the guards."

"In other words, one could expect real fighting to break out here at any time," said the frater.

"As I told you this morning, we already had a fight here when they tried to take me away the third time. And maybe there will be another fight; but let's leave that in the hands of God. Now we have a concern of a different nature. It seems to me that it is connected with that Nález and your visit. He is trailing you, and me along with you. Therefore,

136

we must be clever enough to outwit the whole militia."

"I know you will find a way out of this," commented the frater.

"At least I'll give it a try. Even now I have a plan in mind. We will go out on a sick call, and you will be my server. And we will go quite some distance, even to the hillsides. For I actually do have a sick person out there. It has been over a week since I visited him last. This will be a convenient visit—for as the saying goes, we will kill two birds with one stone. Leave it all up to me. We will first refresh and prepare ourselves for the journey. By nightfall we should be in the hills among the forests, with people who are as good as these upright guards of mine."

"God's will be done, my dear Pavol. I said that from now on I place everything into your hands. I wouldn't want to be caught in the claws of that militia, for I know what that would mean. Therefore, I want to get out as soon as possible. If they should ask for me, you can tell them that I went to the town X from whence I came—that is, if they should ask you about it. But you are so resourceful that you need no advice in this matter."

"While I need no advice, we must have an understanding. For if it should happen—which God forbid!—that they should get one of us, our respective explanations should coincide. For experience teaches that most of the tragedy that occurs in our organized opposition movement is due to the fact that our people do not have a prearranged understanding about slogans and passwords, or that a person shows weakness at a crucial moment. When a soldier notices that talk about a particular event and identical persons differ, he is already in a position to be merciless, for he well knows that he is on the trail of disaffection in the opposition camp, and that he will eventually attain his objective. Therefore, there must be unity in our talks; and let us prearrange our plans. As soon as we make up our package, we will complete our other affairs. And I do believe that everything will come out right. May God help us!"

Hillsiders Defeat the Militia

NEITHER FATHER PAVOL nor Frater Ján packed very much, in order not to be conspicuous. They took along a loaf of bread and a piece of bacon, like farmers going to market or workers going out for a week to a mine or factory. It was not a large packet, even though Father Pavol added some linen. He entrusted the package to Ján.

"You will dress up like a server, and the package under your arm will not be very conspicuous. You will go before me on horseback."

"And how long will our journey last?"

"Not more than an hour, even with a little rest, if it should be necessary. However, we will travel uphill, and our horses may sweat a little. But now we must have an understanding on procedure if anything should happen to separate us. Therefore, remember that you are on your way to town X. If uninvited companions should catch up with you, tell them that you are going to town X tomorrow. That will suffice for the present. By nightfall we will work out further plans, and I do believe that by that time we will be resting peacefully. I don't expect to return to the rectory this evening, for the hillsiders generally detain me—here a confession, there some other consolation to give. One must hear the people and advise them. The people have always been used to accepting advice and help from its spiritual leaders. And now they need it especially. Out there in the hills we are needed more than here at the rectory. For here the people are together, with two priests at their disposal, while those on the hillsides are scattered and cut off from the world."

Father Pavol and Frater Ján had a good lunch of scrambled eggs, with homemade sausage and fresh coffee. Father Pavol prayed, then went off to the church for sacred hosts, in order to be prepared if anyone out on the hillsides wanted to receive communion.

He returned from church in a surplice, accompanied by the sexton. Thus, he mounted his horse, while his cousin was dressed up as a server. This was the traditional way of making sick calls to the hillsides. For the paths were narrow, making it impossible to go by wagon, and one had to travel by horseback.

Father Pavol had been carrying on such ministrations for five full years. He did not send his chaplain out to the hillsides, preferring to do this grateful task himself. He took a liking to visiting the hillsides; such excursions enchanted him. It was a new lease on life for him, full of mysteries and beauty. Hillsiders were a good, devout, hard-working people. Every Sunday they literally swarmed to the church. In clear weather from the belfry one could notice smaller and greater groups of devout hillsiders coming down the slopes.

Father Dubovan loved this people. In church they appeared as a sea of beautiful flowers, made up of shawls, bodices, bonnets, and beautiful aprons—color everywhere, as lively as the fancy of the farmwives who embroidered these costumes for themselves, their children and husbands could make them.

Good and noble hearts beat beneath these costumes. The hillsiders were a people who would sacrifice their lives for a priest or for any of their compatriots. They were a simple people in thought, in attire, and in work. During the days of freedom, the government publicly praised this industrious people, its conscientious payment of taxes, and its loyalty. In the same way now, Father Pavol and his fellow workers admired the hillsiders for their strong opposition to Communism. Great legends were already being created about hillside heroes, how they sheltered the persecuted, how they repulsed communist partisans, and how communist soldiers were lost in the heart of the forests. Hillsiders inspired a holy terror. Every hill and cottage was a threat, for there was no telling from whence would spring up a regiment of valiant fighters.

That's why Father Pavol loved the hills and enjoyed visiting with the hillsiders. And they in turn repaid love with love. The greater majority of rectory guards were hillsiders. They were a tall, healthy people. Their very stature and bodily development inspired fear. And they were all of the same general type.

Now he made this trip for the sake of his cousin, rather than for the hillsiders, and made it gladly. They started out through the yard, and thence reached a wide lane. Wading through a small brook, they reached a pasture, at the edge of which grazed horses attended by four men. These men greeted Father Pavol respectfully and knelt down, for they noticed that he was going on a sick call.

The pathway started leading uphill, and the horses trotted along slowly. But this location also presented an admirable view of the village and the entire valley. One could not see what remained hidden up above, for beyond the pasture were birch, then oak, and finally spruce forests.

Frater Ján looked behind him over the winding pathway over which they were traveling. He looked back towards the village and noticed that there were three horsemen galloping after them. They did not seem to be civilians, and they were in a hurry.

Might they not turn out to be evil companions?

Father Pavol stopped and held the bridle of his sorrel. Turning in the direction of his church, he gazed at the slope of the hill where the horses were galloping.

At this Father Pavol placed two fingers to his lips and whistled. The horse herdsmen, who had just recently greeted the priest and knelt down, heard the whistle. Frater Ján saw them make a beeline for the shrubbery. Pulling out saddles, they whistled back and mounted their horses. Father Pavol whistled three more times. From the opposite hill appeared horsemen and answered the melody, "They Chased Me for Three Days." This was a predetermined signal. There was also a whistle from another direction, one according to the melody of the song, "When I Went Up That Bystrica."

"We are saved, if there are not too many soldiers. But even if there should be too many, I know these paths well. And there are hiding places in the woods nearby. We will hold out. Have your revolver ready for any emergency."

The frater did not like the idea of using a revolver, but it was not in vain that he had tried one out before mounting his horse. One of the guards had wrapped the barrel of his revolver into a thick rag, and thus he had to shoot inside of the stable until he was able to hold the gun firmly. At first he trembled, but the guard encouraged him: "You are not going to kill, only defend yourself, if that should be necessary."

The frater accepted this solution, and now when danger was at hand and he had heard the various signals, he gained courage and daringly squeezed the shining revolver.

"Now let us proceed; but don't force the horses, for that will not get us anywhere. Just trot your horse along at a normal pace. Our boys know what's going on and will take care of the soldiers. They have often matched their strength with them."

Father Pavol had scarcely uttered the last syllable when the sound of sharp firing reached their ears. First, as though a shot from a gun or a rifle; then rattling, furious machine-gun fire resounded from the sides of the pasture through which had trotted two horses bearing Father Pavol and his cousin.

Both of them looked back, but saw no one, neither soldiers nor their defenders. The soldiers had wanted to cut Father Pavol off; but evidently, the guards noticed where the soldiers' horses were going. Therefore, the firing sounded closer to the hill. Then all was quiet for some time. Only riders from the opposite side galloped over close to the pathway. And again they gave the signal, according to a prearranged melody.

Both the frater and his gray mount sweated. Father Pavol became more alert and constantly looked around for unwelcome companions. Firing broke out again. The horsemen, who had just galloped over from the opposite side, now cut the pathway several hundred meters below Father Pavol and his cousin and proceeded in the direction from whence had come the sound of gunfire.

"This may be rather dangerous," said Frater Ján.

"It may be, but there is no call for fear. Leaving the pathway will allow us to elude the soldiers more effectively. We can rest our mounts and ourselves in the thick birch grove nearby, and at the same time notice what is going on. It seems to me that the firing is being drawn farther away, as though the soldiers had entered the neighboring valley. Evidently, they have struck the trail. Let's hope our guards will intercept them before they run into the crosspath which leads from the neighboring valley to the one we have been traveling thus far. Let's keep our fingers crossed."

They brought the horses over to the birch grove, tied their horses to strong trees, and started following the gunfire. Father Pavol dared to take a few steps towards the vale. As he did so, the machine gun again started barking. He did not know whether it was from the soldiers or the hillsiders.

He worked his way through the birch thicket and tried to take in the view of the valley. He found what he was looking for with his field glasses. He clearly saw the soldiers in uniform, each with a machine gun, grenades hung about their necks, and a belt of cartridges around their waists. Father Pavol whispered to himself, "This can indeed be a fierce struggle. Our guards will probably not be as well armed." He could not see them. They must have been at the slope of the hill, at whose crown he and his cousin were now standing. The soldiers also headed in this direction.

Father Pavol went a little ahead. The soldiers tried to reach the thicket in order to hide themselves; but firing broke out from the side again, so that it was hard for the soldiers to make a move. One of them had just dismounted his horse and was crawling towards the side.

A shot rang out and the soldier moved no more. Maybe he only pretended to have been wounded. On the other hand, he may have gotten what he was looking for.

This encouraged the hillsiders. They renewed the firing, and in a short time started charging the soldiers. The soldiers turned in the opposite direction and sought safety in a neighboring wood lot.

But a known signal sounded also from this wood lot, followed by the racket of machine-gun fire.

There were guards also there, protecting Father Pavol. The soldiers reached a lone tree in the vale; and, casting themselves on the ground, with leveled machine guns they awaited developments. When they thought their opponents were motionless, they started crawling towards the wood lot. But this was their misfortune.

Father Pavol and Frater Ján observed that the soldiers were cut off on the one side by the guards who had been pasturing their horses there not long ago, while their friends came out of the wood lot from the opposite side. The guards came right up to the soldiers and ordered them to surrender. Father Pavol saw how they threw down their machine guns, grenades and ammunition, and with upstretched hands approached the guards.

All of a sudden there was gunfire. Father Pavol heard several indistinct outcries. He himself became frightened; but he hung on to his field glasses and observed what was going on. The men who had been coming out of the wood lot scattered and seized the two soldiers, while the group which had come from the slope of the hill, on which Father Pavol was located, swiftly turned in the direction of the wounded soldier, who had taken advantage of the confusion and aimed into the groups. But he missed—at least Father Pavol did not notice anyone being hit—for they all moved and the firing was repeated.

The lone soldier stopped shooting. Maybe his machine gun was out of commission, or he himself may have been seriously wounded.

The men closed in on him. When they were altogether

143

near, the soldier pulled out his revolver and hit one of the hillsiders. But at this a shot resounded again from one of Father Pavol's guards, and now the soldier was totally disabled.

When the boys had all three of the soldiers in custody, they took them and their horses down to the vale, entered the thicket and started whistling according to prearranged signals. Firing ceased. Father Pavol answered, and in a short time they met.

The two sound soldiers were tied up, while two men carried the seriously wounded soldier so that Father Pavol could tend to him as soon as possible. He had medications along; and, binding his wounds, he ordered two hillsiders to take him as quickly as possible to the nearest home, where the landlady would look after him.

"Do not harm him. I will visit and have a talk with him."

"And what about these scoundrels?" asked a dark-complexioned hillsider of Father Pavol.

"Take these to the place where we last rested up. They will take good care of them there. A little home imprisonment will not hurt them. But do not harm them, only reprove them. Our people know what to do with them. Humanely, but strictly. Them also I will see, if not today then tomorrow."

Two hillsiders led away the bound soldiers, and Father Pavol and Frater Ján remained alone with the remaining five guards.

Two of them went ahead of Father Pavol and three walked a good three hundred meters behind.

Frater Ján now admired his cousin even more than he had heretofore. He regained his composure, and his heart beat normally again. And he resolved to follow Father Pavol in opposition to Communism.

Father Pavol also thought things over—but not about what had just happened, for he had already gone through more trying moments. His concern was about his cousin; that he fail not nor be broken down, but hold out and save himself, to be a credit to the family which had always lived peaceably and had served God, the church and the people so faithfully.

Father Pavol sighed. No one heard him, for the frater walked some distance ahead and the horses clattered beside the pathway. The birch wood lot became thicker and the air clearer. The sun was already settling over the hills. But this was a most pleasant season of the year.

They had scarcely gone several hundred meters when Father Pavol called to Frater Ján to stop, and gave the guards the same signal. Those in front stopped, and those behind Father Pavol came up. All were curious to know whether he was changing his plans. Father Pavol only made a motion that they rest up. For the fighting had tired out the guards, and he and Frater Ján had to talk things over. He was especially concerned for his cousin, for this was all new to him, and there had been too much of it for one day.

"We will rest up. The horses also need rest, and we will refresh ourselves." He ordered the frater to bring out the lead-encased bottle of wine. He opened it and poured out wine into the lid covering for each of the guards; then for Frater Ján, and finally for himself.

"They chased us around a little," commented hillsider Matúš.

"But it wasn't so very bad," answered Juro. "Only Martin was wounded a little. But for all that, we have the three of them in the cage."

"Indeed, and how is it with Martin?" asked Father Pavol.

"Nothing serious. Just a little blood below the knee. A scratch, as it were. Come over here, Martin!"

The tall hillsider appeared before Father Pavol. He had powerful arms and a big mustache. He sweated a little and seemed to limp on the left foot.

"Does it hurt, Martin?" asked Father Pavol.

"Not at all! It's only as if a weak pup had bitten into the flesh. Do not fear for me, Father. I heal easily. It was worse during the war, and also in the engagement with the Bolshevik partisans when they broke into our sheepfold, determined to rob us of it. At that time we had but ordinary guns against a machine gun that they had brought in from somewhere. But even though they took six of our sheep, and hit me here in the right hand, I came out of it. Not even a doctor was necessary. Mother put on some tallow and some herbs, and in less than three weeks it healed up."

"Thank God, Martin, that you are so courageous and rely so much on your strength. Such people bear every cross more easily. May God bless you!"

Each of the guards took another sip of wine, then the senior ordered: "Back to your stations, boys!"

And they spread out into a large circle and observed from every side, listening intently as they patted their horses, which in the meantime had been grazing on the thick pasture amidst the birch grove.

"This is the pride of our race," said Frater Ján to his cousin. "With such people one is able to accomplish wonders. I would almost envy you for them, if I were not about to join them myself."

"They are valiant youths. They have accomplished much and have saved many of our people."

The frater wanted to say something more, but just at that moment a familiar melody, which he had heard not long before, sounded. It was one of the melodies which Father Pavol had used in communicating with the hillsiders. Someone was whistling out there in the hills.

Father Pavol quickly got up, all the hillsiders grabbed their bridles, and Frater Ján also straightened out.

"Everyone mount his horse," said Father Pavol, before he answered the third whistle from the hill. When they were all mounted, Father Pavol whistled again. But this time he used a new melody. Later Ján asked why his cousin used so many different melodies.

"You will understand it better when such a responsibility falls on you. These are all predetermined signals. One means caution; another is used to question; a third means the conclusion of danger."

"That is a brilliant idea," remarked Ján, satisfied.

Father Pavol gave the order to move more briskly. Occasionally, he would whistle and get an answer from the hill.

They galloped along ten full minutes until they heard a whistle close by. A horse neighed in the beechwood.

They stopped. Father Pavol again whistled, this time a softer melody.

Suddenly, two riders appeared before the group. They had not been in Father Pavol's company formerly. This meant that the hillsiders had already sent them out.

"May God bless you!" said Father Pavol, anticipating the riders. "What do you bring us?"

"Hulina sent us out to ask you to hurry, for the wounded soldier whom the guards had brought to our place is in a bad way and would like to talk to you. He said to ask you to delay not if you are prepared for administering the last rites."

"Neither will we," said Father Pavol seriously. "It is not far; the horses can run the rest of the way." And Father Pavol took his place at the head of the company and raced as fast as his mount would go.

The frater strove to remain at Pavol's side, but did not know how to hold the reins. The horse refused to obey him, galloping along to suit himself.

The hillsiders were masters in horsemanship. Not all of them had saddles, and yet they kept up close behind Father Pavol. One of them also helped the frater to hold the reins steadily and sit firmly in the saddle.

A cold sweat broke out on the frater's brow, and he was afraid that the reins would slip out of his fingers. But he wiped off his right and left hand in his coat, and again strove to imitate the riders, so as not to remain behind altogether.

Father Pavol had no other concern now but to get to Hulina's cottage as soon as possible, to reach the soldier who had asked for him while he was still alive.

The horses ran out into a clearing, and they could already see the first home. It was the Hulina farm. The farmer stood before his home, looking into the forest. And he jumped for joy when he saw the riders, with Father Pavol at their head.

"Greetings, greetings a hundred times over! God Himself must have brought you over."

147

"Where is the wounded man?" asked Father Pavol.

"Out there on the threshing floor, laid out on soft hay. My daughter is looking after him. He is wounded so seriously that I don't think he will hold out much longer. He is already halting in his speech."

Father Pavol dismounted and hurried to the threshing floor. He must have been well acquainted with it, for he asked no one questions but went there directly.

The wounded soldier coughed up blood. His eyes were red and swollen, a sign of the end of life. Just at that moment, he opened up both his eyes and cried out: "I wanted you, Father Pavol! Come here and listen! I am unarmed. I am like a child. I have wandered, and I sinned when I allowed myself to be enticed for such work. It is not work suitable for human beings. . . ."

He stopped and ceased talking. Father Pavol took out medications and smeared his forehead and temples. The man again regained consciousness and brokenly declared: "Hell cannot win out. And I started to serve hell already here on earth. We are defeated, and will yet suffer many defeats."

The soldier's head fell, but this time into the palms of Father Pavol. He held it up and prayed for the poor man.

After a while, the wounded man again opened his eyes and said his last words aloud: "If my dear mother spoke the truth, that it is never too late to return to God and the people, hear my confession. And I ask the forgiveness of the rest of you. Tell everyone you meet that one cannot believe the communists. That is my last will and testament. Tell it also to my wife and children. May they not wander as I have begun to. . . ."

Father Pavol knelt down beside the wounded man, now no longer a soldier, but a faithful Christian, reconciled with God. He gave the sign for all to depart.

The lips of the wounded man moved. He confessed and received the body of Christ. Then, after a quiet prayer, Father Pavol closed forever the eyes of a great penitent.

Imprisoned a Second Time

FATHER PAVOL gathered his company at the barn floor, where the soldier who had apologized to the priest and the hillsiders had died reconciled to God.

Death reigned in silence. Neither Father Pavol, nor Frater Ján, nor any of the hillsiders at Hulina's barn floor spoke. But they did pray.

They tiptoed up to the corpse and tiptoed away on leaving it. They quietly parted with Hulina, and Father Pavol reminded him to wait till they could take the dead man to the village. Then Father Pavol called his cousin.

"During the journey circumstances forced us to talk more than was proper in the presence of the Blessed Sacrament. Now we will avoid conversation till we reach the neighboring hillside, and there decide how to proceed."

The whole company set out on the road, which led from Hulina's farmstead alongside a thick forest. Tall spruce trees filled the air with a sweet fragrance, and it was pleasant for both horses and riders to travel in their shade. The sun was already bidding a last farewell to the youthful group. When any of the party would turn around, Hulina would wave them on for a happy journey.

After some time a small cottage appeared to the riders on the precipice of the neighboring hillside. Juraj Horný did his farming here. There was a meadow around the home, and round about beside it were fields. A forest touched one side of the meadow, while furlongs of rye stretched out from the other.

The riders were silent as their mounts walked contentedly alongside the pine forest. Sounds of barking broke out from Juraj's hillside. They were the sentinels. The hillsides were never without them, for the scattered homes could not be left unguarded. A faithful dog was often better than a lazy farm hand—one of which farmer Juraj Horný also had.

A guard spoke to the dogs. They stopped barking and wagged their tails as if they recognized his voice. The guards turned directly below the cottage and swung to the right, towards Horný. They went on as though they had been invited. But hillsiders never invited anyone. A just and upright man always found shelter with them. They had their own brand of cures for the wicked—and for intruders.

Horný's wife was already home, for she had had to return from the fields first, as usual, to prepare supper for her large household. "It is very good that I came," she said to herself as she looked out of the window towards the forest and saw the riders, among them many known faces, and especially that of Father Pavol.

When the procession neared the cottage, Mrs. Horný ran out of the home and greeted Father Pavol by genuflecting before the Blessed Sacrament. She motioned to the guards to tie up their mounts in the stable, and at once led Father Pavol and his cousin to the immaculately clean front room. High wooden beds had been made up inside it. They were covered up with great spreads, woven and embroidered at home, charming pieces of needlecraft laid out by the solicitous hand of Juraj Horný's good spouse Mária.

The curtains on the four small windows of this cottage room were also embroidered. The color of the curtains blended nicely with the color of the bedspreads. The room itself had been painted a bright blue shade. Actually, it had been whitewashed with lime, into which Mrs. Horný had blended a blue color.

There was a cross on the front wall between two windows, with a picture of the Blessed Virgin on the one side of the cross and that of Saint Joseph on the other. Underneath the cross was a small chest, or cupboard, in which the farmwife kept her linen and clothing for herself and her household. There were several pictures hung up on the side wall, some with groups of elders and younger people, and others with war mementos. One could also see ancient uniforms hanging here. The pictures themselves were already yellowed with age.

Father Pavol entered the room with his cousin, and said half-aloud: "Peace to this home!"

Mária knelt down and quietly asked: "Will it be all right if I make place for the sacramental Jesus on the chest?"

"Perfectly all right," answered Father Pavol.

Farmwife Horný quietly got up and removed everything on the chest, some cups, books and magazines, and her son's flute. She also took the covering off the chest and changed it for a clean one with flowers embroidered on it. The chest looked almost like an altar, for she also placed two lighted candles on it.

Father Pavol placed the chalice containing the Blessed Sacrament on the center, directly beneath the cross.

In the meantime Father Pavol's company entered the vestibule, knelt down and fixed their gaze on the cross and on the chalice. Father Pavol heard the rustling and turned, his countenance lit up with a pleasant smile of gratitude. And he knelt down before the chest with Frater Ján beside him; behind them were Mária and the guards. They said a short prayer, then all got up, and Father Pavol gave the sign to leave.

But all of them did not go away. Two hillsiders remained kneeling. An hour later two others took their places, and so they alternated during the whole night. There was no conversation, only prayer in the front room that night. No one slept there, for the deeply devout members of the Horný household considered it an extraordinary privilege to have such a precious guest among them, One who reigned between two candles. All of them went to confession and received holy communion the next morning. This was a second

Sunday for them. Before they went out to the fields that day, they dressed up in their Sunday best, and Father Pavol gave them the Eucharistic Christ. Frater Ján and his guards also received.

Father Pavol did not leave the room till the evening, when he went out into the yard with Ján. The anxious Mária asked what she should prepare for supper.

"Be not solicitous about us, Mária. We will be satisfied with anything you prepare," said Father Pavol.

Both of them washed up and changed clothing; then two of the guards went out to the field to get Horný.

"Do you need any help, Mária?" asked Father Pavol.

"Don't worry about me. You are fatigued and should rest up."

But Father Pavol's companions, nevertheless, looked over all the containers to see whether there was enough water for the livestock. The well was out in the forest. In order to give Horný a restful evening, three of the hillsiders took up wooden jugs and went out for water.

"In the meantime, we will go behind the home into the garden, Mária," announced Father Pavol.

"As you please. I will call you when the husband comes home, and we will be ready to sit at the table."

Father Pavol went off to the garden, accompanied by his cousin. They sat down underneath a spreading cherry tree.

"How do you feel, Ján?"

"I have gained many impressions. I see that this will be very interesting, and just as serious as it had been in the monastery. In fact, I will be tried more out here."

"Certainly. But do not lose confidence in God, and cling to these upright people, my parishioners. They will help you, even as they help others. As you see, they have hearts of gold."

"They certainly are invaluable."

"Ján, my cousin, this evening we will remain here. Tomorrow I will go to visit a sick person again, and also see our two prisoners. In the meantime, we will talk over everything; and I will leave you here, or if need be, our people will take you farther along. You will be taken to people as good as these are."

"I agree with your plans, dear Pavol. But in order that we may not lose too much time, would you be kind enough to tell me more about your journey to Calvary thus far? I've heard of your experience during your first imprisonment. But you were there also a second time. I am very eager to know about that, also. How did you get there?"

"I thought that you would forget about it. And I don't like to talk about such things. But since you desire it, I will tell you all. Even for this reason, that you may know what awaits you also. For, to a certain extent, you are going over the same path over which I tread.

"As you know, communists and their allies took over church schools already in the spring of 1945. Then they started forcing religion out from all places. They restricted and prohibited the church press, confiscated the property of religious institutions, and even entered bishops' residences to confiscate belongings. Imprisonments followed, and gradually the steel ring of communistic officials was tightened about the church. They came along with their dissenting 'Catholic Action,' and established their own church government. The fight against religion was intensified, so much so that similar persecution cannot be recalled not only in Slovakia but in all of central Europe.

"Gradually they forced out the teaching of religion from all schools. They used their own refined methods to accomplish this objective. They restricted teachers, catechists and parents to prevent Christ from having access to any school. You will yet learn a lot about all. For you will be with a people which has paid for all this in bitter experiences.

"I will tell you only of my own experience—actually not my own, but of how they took action against priests who would not sign a pledge of fidelity to communistic 'Catholic Action' and paid no attention to their orders. You know as well as I do that communists are making the great mistake of thinking that they will break down the church. For the church has her own laws, her own precepts, and God helps

153

her even if she is forced into the catacombs. We get our directives, and naturally they are different from what the communist-elevated prelates and so-called 'patriotic' priests would want to talk us into. For them we pray and continue performing our duties.

"So it was with the teaching of religion. The pressure was great, and sly school directors and managers were ever inventing new plans. Parents were unable to send their children to religious instructions even though they wanted to. There now remained but one alternative: to ask priests and devout laymen to teach children privately.

"This was a good idea. But communists soon found out about it. Therefore, their office for church affairs, which had been daily overwhelming us with directives and orders, now sent us a directive also in this matter. It was a directive more communistically intense than any before it.

"All spiritual leaders were forbidden, under the penalty of the loss of freedom, to teach either in school or privately."

"And did priests remain silent about this?" asked the frater.

"They did not, but nothing was changed. Protests are of no avail against communists. As long as the government is in their hands, as long as the police is behind them, they know no mercy. And so it was now. Priests who sent in a written protest got their names on a new list for the soldiers.

"I also protested—both privately and also in conducting a mass petition-signing action, which I also sent to the communized *Catholic News*. But they made fun of me and publicly denounced me in an editorial as a rebel, stating that I opposed the democratic order and made no contribution for pacifying relations between the government and the Slovak people.

"I knew what this meant. But, nevertheless, I visited families where they wanted religious instruction for their children. When my parishioners learned of this mission of mine, they followed me en masse. I was no longer able to teach by ones or twos. We arranged it so that ten or fifteen children would gather into the bigger homes at night. My chaplain, who liked this idea, followed me and became a zealous apostle, till he was transferred."

"My dear Pavol, you performed a very worthy service."

"I performed but my duty. A sacred duty! But this did not last long. In about two months I received a summons from the office for church affairs in Bratislava. I considered for a long time whether I should go or remain at home. Finally, I decided to go, in order to tell the communists my idea to their very faces.

"But I had no opportunity to do this, for as soon as I entered the office building for church affairs, two soldiers took me in charge. Taking me out, they threw me into an auto and took me to the police.

"I had been scarcely led into the building before I was followed by a person in civilian clothing whose monstrous eyes gave me the best evidence of who he might be. He was an ordinary queer who spoke Slovak but brokenly. But he was also breaking a rod over my back. He beat me mercilessly for about a half-hour, so that I felt blood trickling down my back.

"I held out as long as I was able. To the questions whether I taught religion secretly, I gave no answer. This angered the furious Bolshevik even more. He ordered me to disrobe and lie down on a bench. I refused. Then he hurled himself against me and tore off every bit of my clothing. After that he hit me with a blackjack over the head so that I fell to the ground.

"Then the agent placed a glowing cigarette to the hair under my armpits, and also to another still more tender place. The hair burned, and I felt a burning pain in my armpits and under-abdomen."

"Unheard of!" his cousin interrupted Pavol's talk.

"I gritted my teeth and closed my eyes. For this the agent roared at me and told me to get up and look into the great mirror which hung on the wall. I got up, but put both of my hands over my eyes.

"Even when the queer pulled my hands away, I did not look. I threw myself on the ground and writhed in the agony that I endured, even though at every moment I was resolving not to give out even a sound that would indicate my suffering.

"But he would not let me alone, even as I lay on the ground. The Bolshevik took up a lighted candle and held it close to the soles of my feet. Then he came up to my chest and held it on the lower side. I shrieked, but the merciless agent gave no heed. Chewing on the cigarette in his mouth, he constantly moved the candle higher and higher, at the feet, then the abdomen, till he came up with it to the neck. There he held it till I felt the pain in the beard. Burnt flesh is very repulsive.

"The Bolshevik spat on me and left me there naked. Then he cut off the light.

"I was left alone with my wounds, on a hard cement floor. The wounds from the cigarette, the candle and the beatings burned me. It mattered not whether I lay or sat up, I felt the pains, and also the blood on my back.

"Mustering up all my spiritual strength, I prayed for the enemies of the church and for all those who suffered even more than I. I could not sleep, only dream, and with prayer I banished all the thoughts that were overwhelming me.

"Suddenly the door opened. The light was put on, and I could already hear the coarse and unpleasant voice of my tormentor. He roared at me, asking whether I had improved and would confess that I had 'transgressed.'

"I did neither answer nor say a word, although I knew that would only make it the worse for me. But I would not betray anyone. For it was not only I who was concerned, but those whom I had taught. And that was my whole village, all my parishioners. And they did not deserve such a deal. A person alone can go through an ordeal more easily than an entire village. Therefore, I said nothing, neither yes, nor no.

"The enraged Bolshevik grabbed me and hit me over the temples with a blackjack so hard that I fell into a forced sleep. I fainted. After I know not how long a time, I came to, and found myself in a narrow cell. Beside me was that refractory queer, and with him yet another. They woke me with a piercing light, which they placed before my eyes. I sat on the floor beside the wall. The light fell directly into my eyes. 'You will sit that way and look directly into the light,' ordered the Bolshevik.

"Again I said nothing. They held me before the light for a long time. When my eyes grew faint and closed involuntarily, they both roared at me, beat me over the back and hit me over the face with closed fists, so much so that I was covered with blood.

"But I held out and remained silent. God helped me. They beat me up also the second and the third day. But they didn't want to kill me—so I think. When they saw that I was exhausted and utterly played out, they stopped. But who knows whether they would not have renewed the beatings had not reaction come from my parish?"

"What happened?" came the question from Frater Ján.

"Two of my courageous parishioners had also come along with me to Bratislava. They wanted to be sure that nothing would happen to me. When we came before the building of the office for church affairs, a soldier asked for our summons. I had mine, but my parishioners did not. He allowed me to enter the building, but kept them out. Neither entreaties nor threats availed. The soldier did but his duty.

" 'Should I have you taken away?' he shouted when he thought they were importunate. I then told my parishioners to go about their duties, stating that we would meet at the railroad station at such and such a time.

"When I did not return to the station at the agreed time, and they could not find me there even two hours later, although they had constantly watched the trains which were leaving in the direction of Zemianska Huta, they thought that something was up. Sadly, they returned home and said that they couldn't find the rector. And when it was verified that I was not at the rectory, neither the first nor the second day, they were certain that I was in danger.

"Therefore, they met with three other courageous and faithful parishioners one evening and laid plans to help me out. They did not go to Bratislava, for they considered that useless. There they would have been seized and imprisoned, even as I had been.

"They made provisions for helping me on the spot. Late that night they went out to Nález's home, awakened him, and took him to his gypsy friend Frolo. They awakened Frolo also; and shoving Nález into Frolo's hut, they acted quickly. They gagged and bound both of them and led them directly to the so-called station of 'people's security,' the communistic police station.

"They did not enter the building, for they had noticed a small light in the guardhouse. However, they crawled up close to it with the bound-up Frolo and Nález. There they threw them on the ground and bound up their feet. One threw some kind of a quilt over them, and then they went away.

"When the soldiers got up in the morning and went to make their rounds, they noticed a suspicious-looking pile before the guardhouse. One of them went up to the pile and saw a piece of paper fastened to the center of the quilt covering. He picked it up and looked it over. There was something written on it. The soldier read: 'If you do not release our rector today, tomorrow all of you will be covered up this way.' "

"And did this help?" asked Frater Ján.

"I think that it did help a little. Three days later I was back at the rectory.

"The soldiers were transferred from Huta, and a group of new soldiers investigated the incident of Nález and Frolo. But their investigation accomplished nothing, and they left me alone. As I told you before, even this is a tactic of communists—not to arouse the people too much, but to stultify them gradually and draw their attention away from those who favor and support them."

"I heard of similar cases while I was at the monastery, but never knew there was so much of it; and I would have scarcely believed it all if you had not told it to me," noted the impressed Ján.

"When there is time, I will tell you more and fill in the details."

158

"I would be very much interested to know why they came to take you a third time."

"Maybe I will tell you that after supper—or tomorrow, Ján. A wagon is rattling along, there is conversation going on in the yard, and evening is coming on. The farmer is probably home. We will go to the yard to greet Horný, one of our most upright hillsiders."

Father Pavol and his cousin got up from under the cherry tree. They went to the yard. They had not yet reached it when Horný solemnly called: "Praised be Jesus Christ!"

"Now and forever more, Amen. May God bless you, Uncle!"

"May He bless you too, Father. Welcome to our place, and come in! Mária has sent me to get you. Supper is ready." Father Pavol stretched out his right hand and grasped Horný's toil-hardened hand. They squeezed their hands and strove to look into each other's eyes in the twilight. Horný's gray hair gave this upright farmer a patriarchal appearance.

The gathering, with Father Pavol at its head, entered the front room. They prayed, then retired to the back room, where wild venison had been prepared for them.

In the Footsteps of Jánošík

THE ROOM in Juraj Horný's home was filled with guests. The children had to take their supper separately in the kitchen. But Horný and his wife were delighted with the visit of Father Pavol and at the arrival of new help in the person of Frater Ján. For Father Pavol had told Juraj at the threshold that this young cousin of his would help the hillsiders, and they in turn would have to hide him if the communists should track him down.

"I will not live at your expense, Uncle Horný," said the frater. "I have two strong hands, and I am a tradesman. I will go from home to home repairing furniture for farmers and farmwives, and am able to make new pieces whenever called upon to do so."

159

"A tradesman will get along very well here. There is always something wanting," answered Uncle Juraj as he gazed affectionately at the frater.

When supper was over, Horný remained seated with his guests at the table, and Uncle Juraj reluctantly began the conversation.

"So it is with us sinful people," he said. "Something ever turning up. We never have peace. Even these hillsides have witnessed many an event, even though one would think that all is quiet here—except for hunting and the Mardi Gras celebrations, which till recent times lasted for three whole days. But now we have misery and more misery. There is nothing to eat, for everything must be given up to the state. Even the crops not yet produced. How then are we to live, let alone enjoy ourselves? If it were not for these hillsides, we would indeed go hungry.

"At one time, some two hundred years ago, conditions were similar. The people lived in slavery. Foreigners lorded over them. They were not masters of their own will. Little wonder then that Slovakia had its rebels. Our Juro Jánošík plundered, but was just in doing so. He took only from those who had an abundance, and who were robbing the working man and torturing him on the rack. Jánošík was a hero and a defender of weak slaves. He fought for them and revenged himself on foreign lords who robbed the country and could not bring about peace; neither would they appreciate honest work and allow a working man to make a living and acquire property.

"That's why Jánošík is remembered in Slovak history. He was hanged but gained the affection of everyone—of the slave and his posterity. These hillsides of ours had Jánošík and his group for guests many a time. As a matter of fact, Jánošík held a consultation with his group several times on our very own hillside. They danced here, roasted a ram, and enjoyed themselves. To this I will add that our hillsides gave Jánošík a personal group which served as his first line of defense, and which brought forth Ilčík, one of Jánošík's cleverest lieutenants. His posterity is still with us."

160

"This is indeed very interesting, Uncle Juraj," enjoined Father Pavol. "I've read a lot about Jánošík, therefore every little detail interests me. Do not let us interrupt you, but tell us all."

Juraj supported his chin with his hand, fixed his gaze absently, and began a new stream of talk.

"And our roots are in relationship with Ilčík. My grandfather's grandfather was Ilčík's first cousin, and belonged to the same group helping Jánošík. That's why they would meet on our hillside and enjoyed themselves here.

"Why, even to this day there is a group of rocks in the wood lot where we get our kindling, underneath which is supposed to be buried a part of Jánošík's treasure. My grandfather used to tell me how as a boy he remembered going to the wood lot to watch on the Feast of Saint John whether that treasure would 'blaze up.'"

"And did it blaze up?" one of Father Pavol's guards asked.

"I can't say for certain, but Grandfather told me that once when they had already left the wood lot without seeing anything, and were halfway home, they wanted to turn back, for it seemed to them that blue flames darted among the rocks. Such flames as old folks were said to have seen on the Feast of St. John.

"With that treasure Ilčík was supposed to have buried his wide belt and his bagpipe. This gave rise to the tale that not only did the treasure 'flame out,' but Ilčík himself played his bagpipe while his band danced about him.

"The facts are these. Till recent times we used to go to this wood lot, where we would have a festival, especially in July. There we would recall Jánošík and Ilčík and his group from this locality, to which belonged also my ancestor—may God grant him eternal glory!"

"May God hear us," simultaneously answered the guards, the wife Mária and the children, who liked to listen to their father, for he rarely talked about Jánošík and Ilčík. Jánošík and Ilčík were great heroes whose names could not be thrown about in wanton talk.

"What more do you know about these matters and people, Uncle Juraj?" asked Father Pavol.

"As long as we are at it, and have occasion to welcome a new member who has been driven out of the cloister, I will tell all, things that even my own sons are not acquainted with.

"My grandfather was fond of mentioning his own grandfather as being Ilčík's cousin. But he was also proud of himself and of his younger brother. For both of them had enlisted in Hurban's army in the year of 1848, and fought against Magyar oppression. It was Stúr, Hurban and Hodža who armed Slovak volunteers, and Huta furnished over a thousand men. About 400 of them were from the hillsides. Hurban came personally to greet the men from Huta and the hillsides for having furnished such formidable help.

"My grandfather was captured, but cut his way back through the lines; and it was inspiring to hear him tell us what all he had experienced in battle and captivity. Our own courage was aroused when he told us how courageously the Slovak volunteers had fought. They were poorly armed, but believed that Vienna would not fail them—as fail them she did, not contributing either soldiers or giving the Slovak people what they went to fight for: their independence.

"This was a great blow to all who had fought to help their people and wanted to bring about order in their own home. When Grandfather felt that his days were numbered, he would often talk about this uprising, and added: 'My Durko, I pray that you will live to see the freedom that I will not behold. Do not hesitate to fight for it. And raise your sons in this tradition, for we are of the heritage of Jánošík. Our hillside is surrounded with the legends of Jánošík. Do not let it go as legends only, but join the fight, even as my grandfather did, and I with my brother. And fight bravely. May God help you!'

"Whenever I visit the cemetery and say a prayer underneath a large cross carved out of a linden tree over the graves of my grandfather and his brother, I recall all these admonitions. And it seems to me that thus far we have been carrying out the wishes of my grandfather.

"He died in oppression. My elder brother and myself have fought for freedom. My own sons have bled on battlefronts, and one of them met his fate at the hands of a godless Bolshevik."

"You must tell us the rest of that," interrupted Frater Ján.

"That I will gladly do, for I know not when we will have another such opportunity to get together. And the years fly on. . . ."

Juraj Horný again fell into deep thought, as though meditating over the last sentence. But he did not allow his thoughts to be interrupted.

"My elder brother," continued Juraj, "fought during World War I on the Italian front. He was on the front lines when that great Slovak champion, General Milan Rastislav Stefánik, once visited them. Brother had a lively recollection of Stefánik's words—that the legion organized in Italy and on other fronts would one day be the Slovak Army.

"And those soldiers on the Italian front wished for nothing so much as to have Stefánik for the first Minister of Defense. But this did not come about. We could welcome Stefánik home only as a corpse. My brother, as a legioneer, was at his funeral. Already there it was said that political rivals had shot him down—non-Slovak rivals.

"I also fought. Not during the war, but during the invasion of Béla Kun's communistic armies from Hungary into Slovakia. They overran the whole of southern Slovakia in the summer of 1919. Many were wounded and several hundred Slovaks were killed. At that time communists killed priests and innocent citizens. I myself saw how they hanged Anton Prokop on a linden tree in Detva, so as to serve as a lesson for us."

"How did you get out of captivity?" asked Father Pavol.

"I wasn't there long. Our soldiers had captured several Magyar officers; therefore, the Magyars were willing to exchange two soldiers for each officer. I was among the fortunate men to be released. But I'd never wish captivity in the communist army on anyone.

"Europe has ever been plagued with wars, one worse than the other. We had scarcely recovered from World War I, and brought things into order, when World War II overtook us. My two sons were in the draft quota when the front shifted to Russian soil. They were taken, and the elder one was sent out as far as the Caucasus."

"Is he here?" asked the frater.

"No. He married into the fourth neighbors, some half-hour's distance away from here. When you meet him, he will tell you all about it. I will only add that my oldest son appreciated that I had told him about Kun's Bolsheviks when he came back from the front. Those out there on the Caucasus were equally bad: many much worse and more inhuman.

"The second son was but in the Ukraine, and not long there. But for all that, he went through a Calvary of suffering at home when, in 1944, Soviet parachutists flooded the Carpathian Mountains here and made it unpleasant for us. My son enlisted as a volunteer against the communist partisans. He went into the hills and had his own well-organized group which made attacks in the deep hills and cleaned out many a Soviet nest.

"But he paid for it dearly. Once he took his servant along on a scouting mission. Soviets cut them off and shot them down."

Tears appeared in Mária Horný's eyes, but she did not cry. In fact she even added: "He died for the freedom of his people. I did not realize it at the time he fell, but I know it now. For if all surrounding people, and even those farther away, had taken up arms against the Soviets as our deceased son had, today we wouldn't be suffering so much; there would be no need of writing about the Iron Curtain; and we wouldn't be living in hope and trusting only in our own strength. There would be peace, there would be freedom. But let's keep on praying that one day there will be freedom also for us."

"That is in order," spoke Juraj seriously. "For we have our

youth and our leaders, such as our Father Pavol here. It is well for us as long as we have them and can profit by our own experience."

Horný seemed to have concluded his talk. Father Pavol began: "You have told us many nice things, Uncle Juraj, but I consider it advisable to initiate this young frater of ours with more detail."

"As you see fit, Father Pavol. I leave that up to you. As you say, so shall it be; we will act according to your will."

"Cousin Ján, I've brought you away out here to the protection of Jánošík's group. There are many of them here, one stronger than the other. It wouldn't be nice of me not to conclude what Uncle Juraj has begun. I have to conclude it, for tomorrow I go back to the village, and I know not when we will meet again.

"Therefore, listen, cousin of mine; and you who are acquainted with the things that I am about to relate, forgive me. For I know not when I should say these things if not at present.

"Uncle Juraj and his wife Mária have yet five other sons. The youngest is twelve years old, but all of them are helping our common cause. The two eldest go for guard duty down to the village, and also are in charge of those who are caught in the village when they threaten our people."

"Even now they are absent, guarding the two who had been shooting at you," quietly said Uncle Juraj.

"As you see, they are in continuous service," continued Father Pavol. "No one pays them, no one solicits them, no one promises them anything. It's parental upbringing, the influence of the father and Jánošík's tradition. Their parents brought them up as real heroes. They've met the soldiers head on many a time; they've often captured arms and ammunition; but not once have they been captured or seriously wounded. On the other hand, they themselves have taken several score of soldiers. The two Horný brothers were also present at the defense of the village when communists wanted to take me away the third time."

"Real blood relatives of Jánošík," said the frater.

165

"That is the honest truth," added Father Pavol. "But look at these here. There are three younger brothers and three girls. All help out.

"When the older hillsiders are guarding soldier captives, or when they are around homes where serious matters are in progress, these six young people carry water for the guards, bring their dinner, fire their stoves, or warm up hidden caves when the weather is chilly. In a word, they take the place of those who are missing from the homes and help the brave youth who are defending our people and its leaders against the plague of Bolshevism."

"This is an excellent organization," said the frater in wonderment. "Whoever thought up the idea?"

"It originated in these courageous hearts—such as Uncle Juraj, his brother, his oldest son and the two younger ones. It is the fruit of healthy farming intelligence."

"You praise us too much, Father," interrupted Uncle Juraj. "If we did not have you, it would be hard sledding indeed. You give us new strength and inspire us with courage. When we have you, we are ready for anything."

"But without you, neither I nor anyone else in the village, our town, the neighboring one, the third one, the fourth, and all of Slovakia, would mean anything. Ultimately, we are but one of you. We are sons of farming parents. Only God has called us to His vineyard. We serve Him and do not disassociate ourselves from you. For you without us, and we without you, would be as a reed in the wilderness. We would dry out, and a slight breeze would break us down."

"And so it is," enjoined Frater Ján. "Only now am I conscious of the fact that one of the boys, then one of the girls, will run out of the room carrying a pot, and return in a while. So that was your performance of duty about the home?"

"Yes," answered sixteen-year-old Fedor.

Just then one of the men who had been praying before the Blessed Sacrament in the front room asked whether Father Pavol had heard the whistle.

"Just now?"

"Yes, now. Listen, he has just whistled again. I do not understand all the melodies."

They all quieted down, and Father Pavol listened at the vestibule door. He recognized it as a signal of danger. The hillsiders got up, and two of them picked up their automatics and rifles and went out.

This pair met one of Uncle Horný's sons out on the pathway. He was returning from the two soldiers whom they had bound up that afternoon.

"Trenčianska kasáreň!" was the password given the oncoming young Horný.

This sufficed to tell the guards with whom they were dealing.

"Is Father Pavol at my father's place?"

"He is."

"And how many of you are armed?"

"There are eight of us."

"I think we will have a lively night of it. Soldiers are coming up the glade. Our front guard has ascertained this, only we do not know how many there are. Therefore, I'd like to have a talk with Father Pavol. I suppose you had better wait here, for I think that orders will follow."

The guards waited for Father Pavol, and Horný's son entered the vestibule. He greeted Father Pavol respectfully, but stood by when he saw the unknown Frater Ján.

"Speak up, son, and tell us what it's all about," his father addressed him. "This is our man, a cousin of Father Pavol. He will remain with us. There is one more of us. A reinforcement and a help. For right here on the hillsides, we will have one of those who fear not the Reds, even as Father Pavol fears them not."

The son repeated what he had told the guards a short time before, and suggested that Father Pavol give the orders.

"I think it will be quite simple. We need but two guards here; the rest you can take with you. They are well armed, as usual."

"That will suffice. We have the advantage, for we know every stone, while the soldiers have to depend on roads and

167

pathways at this time of the night. Otherwise they will either lose the way, or have to wait in the same place till morning. They were coming by the roadway. That's why our men noticed them so soon.

"Therefore, we will leave, Father Pavol. You have nothing to fear, for we will not allow them to come through. If the guards are alert, everything will work out according to a tried formula."

"May God help you! Adhere to your old customs. Guard the citizens from wicked people, but do not murder anyone. For they also are human beings."

Young Horný did not step out, for they heard footsteps and conversation out in the yard. It was the younger Horný. As he passed underneath the windows, he gave the glad signal: "Danger is past!"

He entered the room, and in a single sentence announced that they had four more soldiers.

"Let's hope there are no more," cautioned Uncle Horný.

"The ones that were captured told us that they had no extraordinary reinforcement in the village. Three of them left in the afternoon, four left in the evening, and five more had to remain in the village, lest something happen to them there."

"If they spoke the truth, it could be that way," added Father Pavol. "For there are only twelve of them in Huta. But no one can tell much about them."

"That's why our men remained on guard; and I think that here, too, some of us should remain awake."

"We will guard in pairs," suggested Father Pavol.

"It is not necessary that you and the frater remain awake," said Uncle Juraj. "There are plenty of young people here."

"No, we must do our duty even as the rest, especially as we are here alone."

"You may go to bed, and we will awaken you when your turn comes," said the young Horný, who had come with the last report about the captured soldiers.

Then Father Pavol and Frater Ján went out to the front room to say their night prayers, while Mária made up beds for them in a chamber.

168

"And where will you sleep?" asked the frater of the young people.

"Our home has played host already to more people than this, and we all had room. Just rest comfortably, for we have yet another chamber; and there is enough room for a regiment in the haymow," answered Uncle Juraj.

When he was alone with his cousin, Frater Ján could not refrain from saying: "Never before in my life have I experienced so much in one day."

"You may be rather fatigued, for you did not have a good night's sleep last night, and this lively day may have worn you down."

"Not more than you, Pavol. For I am younger and can take more. Moreover, these talks are refreshing. I have gained a lot of strength and have learned a lot. This is an excellent beginning."

"I am glad that you are contented. I believe that you will continue to like it. Horný and his friends are the people our age needs. Followers of Jánošík! They know what they are doing, and have the courage to do it even today, when there is a soldier trailing their every step."

"A hundredfold thanks for bringing me here, Pavol. Good night."

Attack Within a Church

AFTER THE mass which Father Pavol said in the front room the next morning, using the chest as an improvised altar, he had breakfast with the members of the household. One of Horný's elder sons at once set out for the soldiers, in order to bring back information whether Father Pavol could visit them.

In the meantime, Father Pavol and his cousin Ján retired beyond the garden. Ján wanted to hear about the most interesting incident that had taken place in the church.

"Now that we have a little time on hand, I will tell you of

169

it," began Father Pavol. "I have already told you yesterday that the so-called 'People's Democracy' began the fight against Slovakia's religion in 1945. In addition to what I have already mentioned, they also tracked down the activities of priests. I had made such arrangements that I was able to get reliable reports for a long time. An upright person, who had moved from our town to the county seat X, was instructed to join the Communist Party and to be a zealous enough member to gain their confidence. This plan worked. He gained the information, and we always had reliable reports.

"Only one parishioner, who is now one of our guards, and I knew of this operation. He would go to the town market and always meet our friend at a designated place, where the latter would incidentally give him a paper containing the reports. And when it was urgent, he would even send such reports by postal service under an assumed name. At that time our internal postal service was not yet so much subject to control and censure, consequently, we could trust that no one would seize the reports, even though several of the letters were lost. Nevertheless, every letter was written according to a prearranged code.

"In 1946, all town organization leaders of the Communist Party got the nod to find suitable people who could gather reports about priests," continued Father Pavol.

"Our friend of the county seat X was also selected for this undertaking. He accepted it, and pretended that he would gladly fulfill his obligation. But three days later we sent out the contents of this directive to all known priests."

"What did this communist directive contain?" asked the frater.

"Nothing startling; but nevertheless, it was interesting. It can all be tied up with later provisions against the church and priests.

"For their own secret files, communists wanted detailed reports about the moral life of individual priests. Details about their personal likes. Whom they contacted; and whether they attended outings. Who visited the rectory. Whether they were delicate in their food. How they dressed.

Whether they liked to appear as civilians; and whether they shied from the Roman collar and the cassock."

"That's terrible!" said Ján in a raised tone of voice.

"In itself this would not be so bad. But they had their own scheme for utilizing such reports. For a knowledge of the individual weaknesses of priests would give communists the means to entice them.

"Communists carried these notes about Slovak priests on special cards. And all this information was turned in at the Communist Party headquarters.

"A second duty of selected communists was to trace down the action of priests in churches. This obligation was also entrusted to our friend, and it was in connection with this assignment that he almost lost his freedom. They instructed him to attend mass regularly. He was to note down carefully what the sermons were about. The instruction read: 'Analyze them to see whether the priests are inciting the people to rebel against the People's Democracy.'

"Our friend informed us of this new effort to disable priests; he attended mass faithfully and sent in regular reports. Such reports would read: 'Nothing unusual.' Or: 'The priest analyzed the principles of today's Gospel.'

"The communists noted that our friend was cheating them, and sent out others to check up on him. These in turn gave a different report on the same sermon. Our man was taken to task. But somehow he talked his way out of it—that he was sleepy, for he had had a lot of work the preceding night. The communists admitted that he had had a lot of work to do; but he knew what to do. He disappeared, and is now among us. And his information was invaluable. For it was not until his escape that he was able to give us everything in detail."

Just then Horný's son greeted Father Pavol and informed him that all was ready for his visit to the soldiers. Father Pavol did not like to keep these good people from their obligations; therefore, getting up, he called on Ján to come along.

Young Horný led the horses out of the stable and all

mounted. Horný led the way, and three horsemen followed Father Pavol and his cousin at a distance.

They went all the way above the hill, in order not to attract attention. The road was comparatively good, and the horses rested and fed, so they broke out into a gallop in order to reach their new "mission" as soon as possible.

In less than half an hour, Father Pavol and his youthful company found themselves on a familiar hillside. They skirted the forest and entered a thick larch wood. Then the riders dismounted and picked their way between rocks, Horný leading the way. They descended into a small vale between great rocks. Underneath one of these was what seemed to be an opening. It was a cave. Horný entered, Father Pavol and Frater Ján following. Guards with familiar faces were stationed at the entrance. They greeted Father Pavol and asked about his cousin.

Five steps later, it was too dark to proceed without a light. Young Horný lit one, and the journey was continued. Right behind them appeared a strange view to Father Pavol and his cousin: the two soldiers who had been bound up yesterday lay here on some straw, bound in irons, hand and foot.

Father Pavol greeted and spoke to them.

There was silence.

"Aside from abuse against you, we've not been able to get a word out of them," said one of the guards.

"Neither will *you* get it," shrieked one of the soldiers, who lay facing the rock.

"We don't want anything from you, dear brethren; we only want to inform you that you made a mistake when you chose this occupation," said Father Pavol calmly.

"You are mistaken if you think that by this attack you have gained all." This was the second soldier's answer.

"We have not gained. But we do not revenge ourselves when we get an enemy into our hands, as the communists taught *you* to do."

"We also are communists. Do not offend us," was the soldier's response to the words of Father Pavol, as he turned his angry countenance to the group. At the same time, he

172

made a movement with his hands as if to cast off the irons. "Is such your rectoral love?" he roared.

"That is but a sign of justice, my son," spoke Father Pavol. "Not a hair of your head will be harmed; and I will pray daily for your conversion. And even though these good people bear arms, they understand charity. They love even their enemies. Christian charity neither kills nor carries revenge, even beyond the grave. I know that you are straying, even as many others do, and I also know that you will return. For the tears of your own mothers, and the prayers of those who are imprisoned, and others whose lives you have snuffed out, will bring you back to the right path."

"We are not anxious to hear sermons," shrieked the other soldier, who thus far had said little.

"Are you being wronged? Have you had enough to eat and drink? Are you exposed to an open sky?"

To these questions Father Pavol got no answer—an indication that the guards were fulfilling their duty.

"We have no secret directives, but speak openly and plainly, even before you. For the Scriptures say that yes should mean yes, and no, no. And charity above all!"

These were the last words that Father Pavol uttered in the cave where the soldiers were bound up. He motioned to Ján and Horný, and they departed. On leaving, he shook each guard's hand, reminding him: "Uphold the rule, for Christian justice is above all else."

"We will firmly adhere to it, reverend rector. We will not fail you," said the senior guard, the others nodding assent.

Father Pavol stopped in front of the cave. Looking about, he spoke to Ján: "Now you see for yourself how our men treat those who take up arms against us."

"It is the Christian way; when you are hit with a stone, make the return in bread," said Frater Ján.

"Hot blood cannot always be restrained within a peaceful vessel. Here and there it may happen that our men strike against a cruel enemy; but such cases are exceptional. For not everyone is capable of sufficient deliberation and coolness of nerve to restrain himself. Moreover, there is so very much coercion that a person does not wonder at it.

"But we must proceed. We should part company here, my Ján, for you are to go to another hillside where you will be quartered and find equal approach to all directions. I must go on to visit a sick party and return to the rectory by nightfall, for there is very much work to be done."

"You surely will not leave me without finishing that much promised account of the attack within the church? You have already started it, so do not leave till you tell me the rest of it."

"Very well then," said Father Pavol, glancing at his watch. "I still have a quarter of an hour of time on hand. Therefore, I will conclude it.

"After two imprisonments, the communists watched me very closely. They still watch my every step; but thus far they have not succeeded in dragging me away to torture again. For this I daily thank God and my parishioners.

"Once, when the communistic 'Catholic Action' began operating, our most reverend bishops sent us a pastoral letter, in which they explained their stand on coercion and dissention, and gave us hints on how we should proceed if it should come to the worst.

"At that time the communists had not yet gained all connections between bishops and priests, even though in some bishopric offices their confidants already sat as powers. They would help themselves otherwise; they would have bishops' residences guarded either by soldiers directly, or by detectives. These men would trail a bishop's every move, as well as that of priests coming to and leaving the residence. In other words, the communists laid their groundwork.

"But occasionally, one could still find a decent person, even among communists—that is, one who would not carry out the orders strictly. Such a person would wink with one eye, or even with both of them when necessary.

"Thus it was possible, with the aid of such considerate or non-thorough communists, for the above-mentioned pastoral letter of our archpriests to go out. But there must have been a slip-up somewhere along the line, for after four days, when the letter was already in our possession and we were diligently copying it down and passing it on to the most trusted of our faithful, confidants and underground workers, some of the rectories were being searched. They looked for, but could not find, the pastoral letter. However, in some cases they were successful. Whenever they found it, they would confiscate it on 'orders from headquarters.' Whenever the priest protested, he was threatened with imprisonment. I've had several such instances related to me. The priests concerned themselves would tell me about their experiences.

"When one could argue the matter with soldiers, and the pastoral letter could not be found, it was saved. Thus, I myself debated with four soldiers for two hours. They searched, but could find nothing. Everything was in that library in which we hid out yesterday. No soldier has ever reached it, thus far. When neither petition nor threat availed them, they left.

"True it is that the matter did not end there. They repeated their visit and were stricter than they had been before. They began making threats. But that didn't help either. I betrayed nothing and gave up nothing to them.

"It was Saturday. At night, when I was already getting ready to retire, someone knocked on the door. In stepped the commander of the soldiers. He was very meek and respectful.

" 'My men were here twice and had no luck. I am convinced that you have that pastoral letter, for they have it at other rectories. I know too that you will not give it up voluntarily, for I take it for granted that you have to return the original in order to convince your bishop that you fulfilled your duty. Therefore, I do not want that original; only allow me to make a copy of that pastoral letter. I will do it here at once and leave the original with you. I only want a copy, so that I may be able to tell my superiors that I fulfilled the order.'

" 'No, look here. Your armed men came, and I told them that no one has the right to order me around. I have not changed and will not change my attitude, Mr. Commander.

If you please, I wish to retire. I would be very glad if you would shorten your visit to the rectory.'

"But he was as clever as a snake. He fed me honeyed words, asking whether it wouldn't be better if I had peace, if guards ceased searching, for they are obliged to do their duty and trail me.

" 'That's what *you* think! Conscience means more to me than your guards, your directives and your scrutinies. Impress it on your mind, once and for all, that Rector Dubovan will never betray the church and the nation.

" 'You shouldn't act that way, Mr. Rector. For I too am a man. I also am a Slovak. Neither do I love the Czechs who take the best portion of our bread, occupy the best places in town, in the party and with the police.'

" 'And still you hold out your backs for them, like dumb little brutes!'

" 'Not altogether voluntarily, neither entirely from conviction. One must live, and there's no telling when one of ours can help us.'

" 'You are adept at intercession and are well educated. But I also have an education. I wrong not the soldiers, nor everyone who seems to be a communist. On the contrary, I have consideration for the erring and the unfortunate. For I am a Christian priest. But such talk will not save us when our acts differ. Go whither your heart bids you to go. If you are a Slovak, forsake the communists; if they have indoctrinated you, wander no longer in their godless company.'

" 'That I have been familiar with for a long time, Mr. Rector. I have no time for arguments. You'll be sorry.'

"At this he grabbed the door latch and left without a farewell."

"It seems to me that this was an introduction to something very noteworthy," observed Frater Ján.

"Sunday came," said Father Pavol, "and we prepared for it as usual. I was determined to read that pastoral letter. I got up in the pulpit, read the Gospel, delivered a short sermon, and announced that I had the honor to interpret a precious message from the Slovak lord bishops. I looked over the congregation, up at the choir, into the seats, and in front of the altar. The church was packed, as though for Christmas, or for the Feast of the Resurrection. My confidants had done their duty. They had informed the people that an important pastoral letter would be read.

"I had just read the introduction when I felt, as it were, a jerk at my alb. I looked around and found I was not mistaken, for an unheard-of scene met my gaze. On the pulpit steps was an unknown youth holding a revolver in his right hand and pulling my alb with the left, this time more firmly.

"I looked into his eyes, but he boldly whispered to me: 'Give up that pastoral letter at once; otherwise you will die on the spot.'

"The faithful could not help but notice that something unusual was going on. The people in the church were stirring. I looked around at the altar railing and saw men moving from the front seats, three of them already vaulting the railing.

"The communist traitor was still aiming the revolver at me and demanding the pastoral letter. I looked at him compassionately, for I was not alarmed. I feared not for myself but for him.

"And I was not mistaken, for when he jerked my alb the third time, one of my parishioners behind him grabbed the revolver and jerked it out of his hand. Two of the others got him by the arms, and a fourth covered his mouth with the palm of his hand. A horrible scene took place in front of the altar: the communist kicked, cast himself about, and wanted to shout; the men, in turn, began to slap him about.

"I besought the people to be calm, so as not to provoke a scandal in the church.

"They took the communist out of the church, constantly shoving him here and there. In front of the church he was rushed—not so much by the men as by the women. He took plenty. They held him, despite my plea that they calm themselves and not bloody him up. In front of the church they besought me to read on.

"When I noticed that the crowd in front of the church

was slowly quieting down, I began reading the pastoral letter. It attracted them. But not for long, for in a short while a lively talk again broke out in front of the church. I exerted all my strength and asked the parishioners to be calm.

" 'The whole garrison, armed with guns, is approaching!' shouted one directly on the church doorstep.

"This was already a serious matter. I saw how they were dragging the young communist who had threatened my life back to the church. They took him underneath the choir, and they then carried him down into the crypt. When the door of the crypt was closed, eight powerful men stepped on it.

"By this time the soldiers also thundered up to the church. But they stopped at the door. I kept on, calmly reading the pastoral letter. I also finished saying the mass, and perhaps never before had anyone sung the hymn, 'O Sorrowful Mary,' with such throbbing hearts as did my parishioners this time.

"After mass there was again a disturbance at the entrance to the church. But this time the parishioners were masters of the situation. About thirty of them had gone out of the church through the sacristy. These rushed up to the door before the faithful began leaving the church. They came right up to the soldiers. Some fifty men out of the church also crowded about the soldiers, so that the adherents of communism were enclosed in a pincers movement. They shoved them out of the church, packed like sardines. In front of the church they asked them to give up their arms, and thus allowed them to return to the guardhouse.

"Another group led away the young fallen who had first desecrated our church when he brought in arms and wanted to commit murder directly in front of the altar. They led him away to the hillsides. He was one of the first prisoners of our white legionnaires whom you see here, and who also have custody of the soldiers who attacked us yesterday.

"True, I didn't expect this to end up well. Communists are more vindictive than anyone else. I looked for developments, but not with folded arms. That Sunday afternoon a

178

message was sent from home to home, asking the people be ready for any eventuality. One powerful man was assigned to every tenth home. It was his duty to rouse all if danger should threaten."

Thus far Ján listened with bated breath, not able even to ask a question. But now he spoke: "Not even the imagination of the best authors could work out such plans. Yes, it is a romance written with blood today in Slovakia. And there are so many heroes that one cannot enumerate them all. Each of them is greater than the one preceding. We are not conscious of them, and think that we've lived through the greater part of it all. But sad to say, it is not so. And how did it end up?"

"Well. But it could have ended up badly. For many, very badly indeed. Priests were taken from some of the villages and imprisoned in Bratislava. The faithful saved me. That Sunday was a day of great baptism. It must be regretted that they wounded even that attacker, and that it happened almost in the church. But that afternoon, many more of my parishioners were wounded. But neither did the communists get away easily.

"Around two that afternoon, there were already soldiers in front of my rectory. But the rectory was full of men, and we were able to get connections to the village through the garden to inform them about what was going on. In a little while groups from both the lower and upper ends of the village started marching towards the rectory. Each one left his home just as he was. They did not dress up as if going to church. The majority of the men were in shirt sleeves. But to compensate for it, almost every one of them had some sort of a weapon in hand. Some guns, others but hoes, axes and pitchforks. Likewise the women. They grabbed up pieces of light kitchenware, such as ladles, heavy spoons, rolling pins, and forks. They stormed up to the front of the rectory.

"The soldiers wanted to defend themselves; therefore, they warned both myself and the parishioners that they would shoot. But the parishioners approached through both garden

179

and the yard, attacking the soldiers directly underneath the rectory roof. There weren't many soldiers on hand; hence, they did not dare to shoot.

"This tense state of affairs lasted for about a quarter of an hour. The parishioners would shout at the soldiers; the soldiers, in turn, would insult, now myself, then the chaplain, or those who stood nearby. But there was little talk. The commander seemed to be unconscious of the situation. He was entirely different from the previous evening, when he had visited me at the rectory.

"But he had his reasons for this. He was certain that this time he would win out.

"But he did not win. Automobiles carrying soldiers thundered up. There were some thirty of them, all well armed. They requested the inhabitants to disperse.

"Since no one moved, they made a second request. Silence. At the third request a group of men entrenched themselves in the yard and one of them called out, 'We will not leave the rectory till you pull out.'

"At this the commander gave the order to present arms. Thirty guns, with bayonets attached, glistened.

"The soldiers jumped down from the automobiles. They began shoving the inhabitants, making a pathway for themselves to the rectory.

"But the men did not give way. The first volley was fired. No one was injured, for no one made an outcry. It was probably a volley shot overhead. More of them followed. Some struck and hurt. But they did not cause a panic among my parishioners, and this was their salvation.

"The men crowded closer towards the soldiers. But the women provided the greatest surprise. Some twenty of them brought along pails full of boiling water. And some of them did not hold back, scalding the soldiers. Three of the women were badly beaten up, and the soldiers almost succeeded in taking them away. Two men, who had punctured tires on the soldiers' cars, were mortally wounded."

"Was there any further use of arms?"

"No. There was no more shooting after these first volleys. I started quieting down the parishioners.

"At this the commander of the soldiers publicly asked me whether I would give up the pastoral letter.

" 'I will not give it up,' said I.

" 'We have one from elsewhere, and we will also get yours . . . and *you!*'

"The parishioners began singing religious hymns. I was overwhelmed with tears, no longer afraid for this people. I saw that they would hold out. And hold out they did, there and ever since. They prayed for a long time.

"Shouting into the wind amidst the hymns of the parishioners, the soldiers had to pull out. We had peace. But they did not cease their plans. The entire village maintained its vigilance about the rectory for about an hour. Then selected confidants explained what was being planned further ahead, and the crowd dispersed, constantly looking back at the rectory. I kept blessing them from the window of my rectory office. God did not forsake us.

"Thus originated this strong organization. Guards, confidants, secret hiding places in the hillsides, and all those signals you have heard."

"That is quite impressive," noted the frater.

"Well, I've concluded it, my Janko. I did not want to tell all of it, for it might sound like self-praise. But you also must know what awaits you. Today the communists are even more inventive and recalcitrant than they were then. Now they have no regard for anyone, as you have seen for yourself. Had our men not the preponderance in arms yesterday, there would have been much bloodshed.

"Therefore, be firm and courageous. I leave you in the care of these fighters of ours. We will not be far apart; we will meet again. I will come. Let's begin the journey, in the name of God."

"May God be with you, my cousin Pavol! I am prepared for everything, and you may rest assured that you will not be ashamed of me. Neither will any of these to whom I surrender myself."

181

Horný took the frater under his care, and the rest of the guards escorted Father Pavol. But before they mounted, Frater Ján knelt down and his cousin imparted to him his priestly blessing. Then he embraced him, and each went his way. They went by diverse paths, but their hearts beat at the same tempo. And their paths would meet, even though by roundabout ways. For Ján had deeply imbibed the teachings of Father Pavol, and Father Pavol daily prayed for Frater Ján at mass.

White Legionnaires

FRATER JÁN easily accustomed himself to the new life. The people here were not only good, but could understand his position and even inspire his faith and confidence. And these hillsiders and new companions, who were called "white legionnaires," would encourage him when he got lonesome for the cloister. His workmanship aroused admiration, and his attainments, aside from cabinet-making, soon made him a respected member of the white legion.

Thus far he had met many younger and elder Slovaks. He knew them by name, and also gleaned some knowledge of their past. But he became acquainted especially with their courage and their manner of life.

Just now Frater Ján was starting up the glade so as to reach his new destination, a place about which all legionnaires spoke with respect. They would gather there to talk over their plans; and they would also introduce new members. Since Frater Ján now belonged to this group, he also had to be presented.

On the way over he thought about all that had happened and what he had heard about Uncle Dubovan; about Cyril's visit to him; and about the two subsequent visits of soldiers. During the second visit, there had been a thorough search of the dwelling. But alert Aunt Dubovan had quickly burnt all the letters from her brother-in-law that were in the home.

And when soldiers came to the kitchen, and asked her what she was burning, in the stove during summer weather, Aunt Dubovan had readily answered: "I am preparing dinner." At this she uncovered the pot in which she was boiling beans.

From that time on there were no further reports about Dubovan on the hillsides. Father Pavol had not been there for a long time; neither had he sent anyone else.

Frater Ján leaned against a young beech tree and wiped his sweated brow, for he wanted to spend a little time in meditation. He thought about his good Uncle Dubovan. He had a lot to explain to him, and therefore sought Father Pavol. He could not do it personally; but Father Pavol had probably seen to it.

And somehow, Frater Ján was surprised to realize that, all of a sudden, he thought so much about Uncle Dubovan. But a grateful posterity always remembers good people. And Dubovan was not only a good person, he was a courageous leader of the village. And the entire locality spoke of him with reverence. Many talked about him, and farmers would always add: "We are in need of more men like him. He is solid to the roots. His father was like that." Therefore, it was little wonder that just now, here in the forest, when Ján was preparing to be initiated as a White Legionnaire, he thought about the daring, courage and rectitude of his uncle.

In due time Frater Ján arrived at the Philip hillside. They had here a spacious barn floor, into which they led all who came. No one who was not invited ever came here.

The barn floor was covered with straw, on which sat youths and elder men. All of them were in their working clothes. They had calloused hands, somewhat lengthy hair, and almost all had mustaches; and there were also quite a few beards. Thus, it was hard to tell how old one of them might be. The farmers advised patriots whither to flee if danger threatened; and they shielded them with their very lives when necessary.

One of the farmers sat on an elevated tuft of straw. The

frater was already acquainted with him. He was a giant, with sharp blue eyes. He spoke to them solemnly: "Brethren, we are again gathered together. We have assembled for consultation, and also to introduce ourselves. We have among us a new legionnaire, in the person of Frater Ján. Almost all of us are already acquainted with him, especially how heroically he saved Father Pavol for us. He labors and has a courageous spirit. We've already met him, but he does not yet know all about us. We have tried him for a month, we know of his every step, and are informed of his every word. The council of elders has decided to accept him as a regular legionnaire at this place; and if you so determine, he will at once take the oath to be a faithful member in our ranks."

"We agree," was the unanimous response.

Frater Ján got up and the chairman administered to him the oath; but before beginning this ceremony he said: "I, Father Imrich, a humble servant of the altar and of my Slovak people, beseech you, Brother Ján, to perform your Christian and Slovak duty, by which you bind yourself to fight faithfully against communism and for your conquered people."

And Frater Ján repeated after Father Imrich: "I promise before God and you, my fighting brethren, that I will remain faithful to Christian principles, that I will persevere at your side in uncompromising battle against communism and for unconditional independence of the Slovak people. So help me God!"

"May God hear you!" responded the assembly. Father Imrich, patting the new legionnaire on the shoulder, extended to him his right hand; and all present, one after another, did likewise.

Then Father Imrich addressed the assembly: "I had said that we must introduce ourselves. I will begin the introduction with myself, so that Frater Ján and others, who have not yet had contact with me, may know who I am. I will not speak much.

"I am Father Imrich, for fifteen years a priest of God. Two years I was without a rectory, for a year in a concentration camp. I was in hiding for half a year, when I escaped from the concentration camp; and I've been with you for half a year.

"They took me from my rectory, as they did hundreds of others, because I had refused to sign allegiance to communistic 'Catholic Action,' and publicly confessed unshaken confidence in my bishop. They took me away from my quiet rectory during the dark of night and led me directly to Mučeníky, where were gathered dozens of my altar brethren. Among these were high dignitaries. They would pass on to us hints from the bishops, who in turn had received them from Rome, and thus we knew how to conduct ourselves. There we learned a lot. All the privations, beatings, manual labor and eternal driving were insignificant when compared to the sad actuality that they would not allow us to say mass and pray publicly. But our prelates instructed us how to proceed under such conditions. We said mass, even while we were forced to work. When we would be digging in the garden, and there were two of us together, first one would say the prayers of the priest and the other would serve. There were but few rubrics to go by, and everything was not as it is usually performed at the altar.

"At times ordinary bread took the place of hosts, and wine was kept in a small glass; and this we would touch within our pockets, or under our shirts. After we finished work, we would wash our hands in the cleanest place we could find, if that was possible. At times we had such a small amount of bread that we could not make crumbs enough to give communion to all fellow prisoners who asked for it. But we were always ready for the worst.

"We heard each other's confession, even as we said mass. Thus, we were daily prepared for death.

"We would separate in the same spirit, if by chance they took any of us away, or anyone was lucky enough to escape— as, for example, I was fortunate enough to do.

"I am glad to be among you. Father Pavol, with whom the majority of you are acquainted, and the rest of you will have an opportunity to meet, sent me here.

"Thus far he has been furnishing me with the material to say mass and administer sacraments. But if this becomes impossible, we will provide for everything for a longer stay in the fastness of the hills; and rocks will serve as altars for us even if communists should plunder our villages, imprisoning priests and changing churches into theaters and granaries. That is all, my brethren. I now introduce to you the theologian Mikuláš."

The theologian said: "Communists abolished all seminaries and tried to force on us a theological faculty made up of patriotic—that is, communistic—priests in Bratislava. I was among the hundreds who refused submission. This faculty was scarcely able to get twenty hearers in the beginning; and even at that, not an original theologian registered. Then the communists recruited their own.

"The rest of us were first sent to the army. But in place of two years, we served for three, the extra year being used to force on us a course in communistic doctrine. They did not allow us to return home from service, but took us either directly to the mines or to a water-power station on the Váh River. I also got a job at one of these water-power stations.

"We worked as best we could. And we came in contact with other prisoners. These informed us about events on the outside. Thus I learned of Dubovan, who sent me here. And here I remain. I work, even as do the rest, at whatever is at hand. I shy from no work. In addition to that, I also study. Father Imrich is my theological professor, and I hope to receive the sacred orders of priesthood in two years."

"As long as we are dealing with students, I will introduce to you Brother Stano," said Father Imrich.

"I am numbered with the younger set," declared Stano, "but consider it a great honor to be in your midst. In the year 1945, I was among the organizers of the demonstration in Bratislava against the inhuman treatment of Jozef Tiso, whom they brought back in chains as though he were a criminal.

"At that time they imprisoned me and beat me to a bloody pulp. Behold, here I have four teeth missing!" He showed

186

his upper right gums. "And here on the left hand, look—a scar several centimeters long!

"After six months of imprisonment I escaped to central Slovakia and joined a group which published illegal journals. Some of these persons later came to you and are now among us."

"And you, Matúš, are one of them. Is it not so?" asked Father Imrich.

"Yes, I am," said a stout young legionnaire with a black mustache. "In the year 1946, they caught me passing out leaflets against Communism and beat me up so hard at police headquarters that I was seriously wounded for three weeks. My feet were actually rotting. After many petitions they allowed me to go to my grandmother. She almost died when she saw what a condition I was in.

"Without my knowledge, she went to see the president of the Democratic Party. But he did not give her a hearing, and did not even answer her later written request. That's the kind of a democrat he was, selling out Slovakia to the communists!"

"And we still have some students, is it not so? How about you, Emil?"

"Communists could not win me over, and they won very few who had studied during the existence of the Republic of Slovakia. They called me a 'reactionary,' and when they learned that my father was a merchant, they would not even consider my reference. Later they seized my father's property and forbade me to compete for any kind of state employment. I escaped to the hills, found you, and am happy to be among you."

"This is Brother Svorad," announced Father Imrich.

"I am a worker. I have carried the card of the Slovak Christian Workers Union for twenty years. And I will never throw it aside. Before I die, I will hand it over to one who will be able to take care of it till the people are freed.

"As you know," continued Svorad, "Christian workers had a strong organization. We were opposed to Marxism and Communism, and based ourselves on Christian principles.

187

We were a workers' movement, but not class-conscious and destructive. We always considered the Slovak farmer, the mechanic, the merchant and the office worker as our brothers, whose help we needed just as much as they needed ours.

"And if what communists are doing in Slovakia hurts anyone, it hurts *us!* We brought forth the first great sacrifice. Our president, an honest laborer and our deputy, František Slameň, was the first to fall victim under the murderous weapons of communistic conspirators who attacked the peace-loving people of Slovakia in 1944. Do you recall that, brothers?

"At that time we decided how to proceed. We go in two directions. Fathers and providers for numerous families seemingly entered the Communist Party, so as to hold their jobs and inform the rest of us about what is taking place. We single men, and those having no children to support, chose the path of resistance. As long as it was possible, we organized strikes and sabotage. When their inspections became more stringent, and they started transferring workers from place to place, many of us escaped. Some of us are beyond the borders, others here and in other Slovak hills."

"I thank Brother Svorad. He performs an invaluable service for our cause. Thanks to his connections, we have very good reports about the intentions of the communists. We've escaped them more than once, only because Svorad's connections function so excellently.

"This is Viktor, from Bratislava. Originally you were a druggist, were you not?"

"Yes, a druggist. On that fateful April morning of 1947, when it was noised about where they were to bury the body of murdered Jozef Tiso, I was in the group which carried flowers to the grave, and then also prepared several slogans and pinned them to the wreaths.

"The police scattered us three times. But we thought we could hold the place effectively, until they made a road over the grave—if it is actually there. For two days they rolled heavy rollers over that place, scattering gravel over it, as though they wanted to obliterate every trace of this great priest and statesman.

"But the groups of youths and elder men increased day by day at the cemetery. Then they made use of the cavalry to disperse us thoroughly. I was among those whom they imprisoned at the third conflict. I was imprisoned for five weeks. They beat me up, even as they beat up the rest of you who have experienced communistic imprisonment.

"When I regained my freedom, I did not even return home, but went directly out to relatives in the country. From thence I went to Zemianska Huta, and afterwards came here."

"We priests will ever testify to the greatness and sanctity of President Tiso," added Father Imrich before he introduced Tomáš, who had been one of the officers of the Democratic Party.

"To my sorrow I must admit," said Tomáš, "that I was very much disappointed in my party, even though in the years 1945 and 1946 there was no alternative other than to seek refuge in its framework. I had the opportunity to look into its apparatus and understand its deputies and high functionaries.

"Among them were also good and honest people. But they could never get the floor; and whenever they dared to do anything, communists would demand their freedom. And the saddest part of the whole matter was the fact that the party was getting rid, one by one, of its best workers, and there was no respect for the authority of the ballot.

"It was most painful for the party and its members to note that there were many communist agents in the rank and file as well as in the very leadership of the party. Democrats were happy that communists were joining them. But they were not joining them out of love for democrats, but on orders of the Communist Party, so that the Democratic Party be dissolved. And the very center of the party contained members of the Soviet secret service.

"Finally, a person could not tell with whom he was in contact. For it was clear, after they had imprisoned several deputies and two chief secretaries, that only allies of communists and communists themselves could maintain themselves at the top."

"It is a very sad chapter in postwar Slovakia. Treachery upon treachery," concluded Father Imrich.

Now Colonel Stopko spoke. "I was a Slovak colonel—and still consider myself one. After the year 1945, they would not allow me to serve my country. And I am glad that I didn't have to take orders from communists. Actually, I accepted involuntarily when they cast me in chains and threw me before the 'national' court simply because I had led honest Slovak soldiers in the year 1944, when Soviet partisans overran Slovakia. I was imprisoned for three years, and then escaped from a hospital with the help of one of you—who is here and well knows the conditions in the army after the year 1945."

"That is Brother Simon," said Father Imrich.

"I entered the army in 1946," declared Simon. "Among my superior officers were but two Slovaks. The rest were foreigners. Every unit of the army had its so-called 'enlightened' leader. In other words, he was a political commissar who had daily lectures for officers and soldiers. He always spoke of the current political situation, analyzed the principles of Marxism, Leninism and Stalinism, sang the praises of the 'glorious battles' of the Soviet army, and never forgot to attack the 'Western imperialists.'

"Ordinarily, all higher political members were non-Slovaks. And officers were always subject to political instructors, even though these were lower in rank. The army was not subject to the leadership and orders of its officers, but to the leadership of the Communist Party. In this connection, it must be mentioned that even if the commander should be a high-ranking Slovak officer, his political lieutenant was always a non-Slovak.

"Another interesting aspect of the army was the continued transference of units. They did not trust Slovak soldiers. During the time of the theatrical court proceedings—as for example in the case of Doctor Jozef Tiso—entire garrisons of Czech soldiers and police marched out to Slovakia. Then they introduced the custom that Slovak soldiers were sent to Czech barracks and Czech soldiers were sent to Slovak

190

barracks. Thus Slovakia was deprived of its own defense, for under present conditions, ninety-five per cent of Slovak soldiers serve in Bohemia. And there are no higher Slovak officers in the Ministry of National Defense who might be able to seek rectification."

"That is a communistic way of sowing dissension and hatred," added Father Imrich; and at once he introduced Blažej. He said: "I was one of those forcibly moved from Bratislava. Communists announced that Bratislava was to be rebuilt into a socialistic city. And since the carrier of socialism and the common classes have no adequate housing, and Bratislava still contains many people burdened with a middle-class past and religious fanaticism, it will be an easy matter to make room for workers. Therefore, they began taking dwellings, one by one, from anyone against whom a neighbor proletarian but pointed a finger. Thus, they expelled no less than fifteen thousand from our capital city and sent them out to the most unproductive parts of the nation. These people would get no more than a single room for a dwelling, even though the family contained twelve members.

"Some of the inhabitants begged the officials that their dwellings not be taken away from them. I would guess that I had met about fifty Slovaks who had tried to change this decision of the secret housing commission—which, of course, was nothing more or less than a part of the communistic apparatus; but they would not oblige anyone. The inhabitants would go from office to office, but no one would listen to them. Finally, they even imprisoned some of them.

"It is characteristic of communists to camouflage everything so that the citizen may not learn the truth about the men behind the action. When one went to seek justice at the Central Committee of the Communist Party, he was sent to the Commissariat of Internal Affairs. There they would make excuses and send the afflicted man to the housing office; but they would not take up the matter even there. The party would get a directive to see the local national committee, and this committee would send the citizen to the Country National Committee. There, too, they got rid of their obligation by saying that this matter was under the supervision of the Central Committee of the Communist Party.

"It must be mentioned that country inhabitants behaved admirably towards the people from Bratislava. They helped as best they could. Their charity is beyond description. I did not long remain at the country dwelling assigned to me, for I could not long remain at the village. Therefore, I chose voluntary escape into the hills."

Father Imrich wanted to add something, but in stepped the guard on duty before the barn floor and announced: "A messenger has arrived from Father Pavol. He brings in a report and some help. He says that serious events have taken place. The messenger wishes to speak personally with Father Imrich and Frater Ján."

"Brethren, we will conclude this assembly for a while," said Father Imrich. "In about an hour or two, we will meet again. Tomorrow we will again resume briskly, as we have disrupted our work today. May God be with you!"

Father Imrich and Frater Ján went aside with the guard, and their footsteps resounded over the stone yard.

A Sad Report

FATHER IMRICH and Frater Ján returned to the barn floor in an hour, and the introduction was resumed.

"We have among us a former church trustee from the cathedral of the town X," said Father Imrich.

Church trustee Víto recalled: "It was in the spring of 1950 that soldiers came to the cathedral. They forced their way into the sanctuary and the sacristy and took all the chalices, monstrances and other valuable vessels used in church and liturgical services. There were two old men in the church at the time. They first took them out in front of the cathedral, then led them along to town, where they seized whatever they could lay their hands on.

"It was not till he was imprisoned that one of the parishioners learned from these two elders that the soldiers had taken them along. And when the time of their arrest was learned, it coincided exactly with the time when valuable material turned up missing at the cathedral."

"There are many similar blasphemous incidents in Slovakia," concluded Father Imrich. "Among us we have also an upright artist, a singer, who will tell us something of the conditions in the theater under the communists."

Timotej made his account brief: "The Slovak National Theater is subject to strong pressures by communist leadership, in Bratislava, as well as in Košice. This leadership tried above all to rid itself of Slovak actors and singers, even though they were talented. Communists forced in their own people, performers without sufficient experience and very much below standard. And once a non-Slovak got a leading part, it was useless for Slovak artists to compete. They did not get parts. Thus, the theater and the opera not only failed to serve the purpose of true culture, but were even used for denationalization, for the use of the Slovak language is progressively declining on the stage. And it is not even necessary to mention the fact that only propaganda plays are selected.

"And to speak up against all this? That certainly would mean joining the ranks of bourgeois nationalists! That's why even a first-class communist like Andrej Chmelko, who is still director of the theater in Košice, did not protest when the theater chief Jozef Bartl consistently refused to accept Slovak artists. And we have more such Chmelkos.

"The drive against Slovak artists, not only actors and singers, but playwrights and musicians as well, is but the result of a well-thought-out Bolshevik plan to corrupt the spiritual aspirations of the people, to poison them slowly and surely, to kill in them the sense for the higher things of life and the consciousness of higher ideals, and so make of them but servile instruments instead of human beings. Communists can then use them as they see fit, in order to take over country after country, and finally the whole world."

"Slovak artists tread the same road of Calvary as other segments of our people," noted Father Imrich as he gave the floor to Dominik, who had formerly held a high position in state administration.

"I am one of the thousands and thousands of individuals who worked in administration for many years. But from the very beginning, we were a thorn in the side of the communists. Therefore, they started removing us from our original positions, even though some of us had had as many as thirty years of service behind us. Whether it was in great industrial undertakings, or in state, district or community offices, ninety-five per cent of the Slovak people who had lived freely and decently during the administration of their own Slovak government were now transferred to physical labor. Much of this was of a type which all communists would shun, because it was hard and paid very little.

"The new regime began changing Slovakia from its foundations. They want to make our country an industrial nation. To this end they began to transport machinery from Bohemia and to build factory alongside factory. All of a sudden, they said there was a shortage of labor. Therefore, officials were forced to work in factories. But as laborers only. Official, and so-called technical, positions were taken over by foreigners. These had come along with the machinery.

"Wherever one came upon new industrial developments, there Slovak was no longer spoken. Workers were silenced, and those who gave orders were foreigners. These 'indispensable specialists' sent out to us in Slovakia received their orders directly from the Communist Party. They were not only overseers for workmen, but also political instructors, spies and agents. The more they transferred Slovak officials into factories, the more foreign 'specialists' crowded in.

"A certain friend with whom I had become acquainted in the factory told me: 'I had worked for a national establishment which contained four factories. All told, they employed some thousand workmen. All of a sudden, we got a circular from Prague in which we were told, with honeyed words, what must be done for the country and the state. At the conclusion of the circular it was ordered that our establishment transfer ten of the highest officials to manual labor.

" 'This was done. But two weeks later, it was required that we transfer two more. This also was done.

" 'A month later we got a circular from the chief director of Prague, in which he stated that our establishment needed specialists. There are plenty of them in Prague. Therefore, they wanted to send them out to us at once. And they *did* send them—non-Slovaks, directly from Prague—to occupy the very places which had been recently vacated by the Slovaks.

" 'Later, I learned that my place was also taken over. Not, however, by one man, but by six! Therefore, I had been doing the work of six, but receiving the pay for one. Of course, these six were all Czechs.

" 'Originally there had been sixteen officials in the entire establishment. When they transferred them to manual labor, some of us fled: eighty-five foreigners, with salaries as high as we had been getting, took over. Such is the evolution of communistic aristocracy!'

"That's where my friend ended up. Of course, he did not save himself, for he was transferred to manual labor, even in the smaller factory. Originally, he had been a legal advisor. First, they had him sweeping up the factory; then they worked him in as an electrician.

"Every transferred official, whether an attorney or an otherwise educated and meritorious worker of long standing, was allowed to do only such work as communists pay the highest tribute to—*on paper*—with pick and shovel, sweeping the factory, cleaning canals, and serving as private servants for communist chieftains.

"Why would they transfer such persons to manual labor?

"This was the principle they worked on: They wanted to isolate the self-conscious intelligentsia and remove it from the position of leadership! They could always find even a formal excuse. For example, they accused me because I had dared to say that, during the existence of the Republic of Slovakia, every citizen could live decently, tobacco was plentiful, and even the lowest-paid officials received enough to be able to buy decent clothing and still had enough left to support even a sizable family.

"This they considered retrogression, Fascism, and conspiracy against the People's Democracy. And I had to go to the factory.

"It is evident what the communists aim to achieve by this: They want to flood Slovakia with foreigners, so that they can force out and destroy all intellectual people and reward obedient communists who will slave for them and fulfill all their orders.

"Therefore, it is little wonder that the Slovak intelligentsia is dissatisfied with this regime. Outside, beyond the borders, there are over ten thousand Slovaks who have succeeded in escaping from this hell. As reports have it, a good seventy per cent of our exiles in the West is made up of intellectuals —that is, priests, teachers, professors, attorneys, doctors, engineers. And how many of us are in the hills, and how many secretly work against the communists even in factories! Foreigners have flooded our factories in order to transform our people. But this will have also an opposite effect. Former officials influence the working classes."

"One wedge is forced out with another," said Father Imrich. "Our people will find themselves. Foreigners once thought of us as a neglected, ignorant people. Our thousand-year-old Christian tradition is constantly with us. It is our mainspring. And the world will yet hear a lot about the people of Slovakia.

"Brethren, we have but one more to hear from. What we have heard thus far testifies to the fact that we did not come out to the hills in vain. We are preparing. We did not come here for personal convenience or individual safety. That would be a very limited standard to go by. We are here to *help*, to stir up an anticommunistic spirit, and to tell our brothers and sisters here and beyond the border that no sacrifice is in vain. As you know, one of our methods of working is to inform the people at home and beyond the borders.

"Our radio transmitting stations serve this purpose. Today we broadcast from one part of the country, tomorrow from another. Transmission takes place from sites where no communist ever trod. We send out reports for our people at home so that they may know what is going on in the world. For the communistic radio and press tell them nothing of interest. And they either silence or twist about every truth.

"But our transmitters also inform our people beyond the borders. In this manner, they serve as a good connection, which speaks for thousands of messengers. We prepare for the passage of those whom we send out West. And there is yet a whole file or other services about which you know, and into which you will be progressively initiated.

"We are a resistance movement. We are legionnaires who make themselves felt by the communists wherever their arm strikes. A tough Slovak people will not submit to terror, even if it were still more crafty and strong.

"We co-operate with Poles, Ukrainians, Romanians, Magyars, and other underground resistance movements who have the same objective we have. We seek friends behind this Curtain of great sufferings, even as our free brethren seek them in the West. And we believe that the West will hear us and come to our aid at the right time and with the proper personnel."

The clear language of Father Imrich electrified all. For it seemed to them that they were hearing a priest from the pulpit as well as a soldier at the front. He was a courageous fighter who led his legion according to the laws of honor.

"We have yet among us Brother Medard, a Slovak farmer."

"A farmer has not much to say, brethren," spoke Medard. "They took everything away from me. Not only from me, but also from my relatives and fellow citizens. They have plowed down our traditional line fences, and they would also plow through our hearts and turn our souls from God, from the soil of Slovakia, and from all that gives the Slovak village its sacred and patriarchal character.

"Communists are mistaken. For the Slovak farmer has

never given up in the past and neither will he be broken now. Our language maintained itself during trying times. Now faith, and everything connected with our lives, will ever maintain itself in the hearts of farmers. And all of Slovakia is rural. Even those laborers once worked in the fields, and high officials also originated from small Slovak villages. And in that I think we are fortunate, for it is the salvation of our Slovak people.

"We farmers also help. We enlist in the White Legion and do our share. I would want to remind all you who send out reports beyond the borders and lead people 'over to the other side' not to forget one thing: Tell them over the radio what we hillsiders here have advocated for ages, 'We want nothing more than what belongs to us!'

"Do not explain things this way and that, turning them about and wrapping them up in gold. But let everyone understand: Slovaks *hate* Communism. They fight and will continue to fight against it, as long as there is a single communist remaining in the world. But Slovaks also want to be free. They seek no special privileges, only what belongs to them—their own government, our own Slovak government, and peace with all neighboring peoples."

"This is clear language and the White Legion adheres to it," said Father Imrich. "Is there anyone against the program advocated by Brother Medo?"

No one was against it, but all cried unanimously: "We agree!"

"We are coming to the conclusion of our meeting today, brethren," again began Father Imrich. "But we still have something on the program. A short time ago we had to absent ourselves with Frater Ján. It was a serious mission. And you will all hear of the very sad report.

"I will soon introduce to you a member of the Dubovan relationship, young Ludo, from Bratislava. He is an upright young man. He is enlisting with us, and I do believe that we will get a strong reinforcement. But more about this later. Now we will hear firsthand what he wants to tell us.

"Brother Matej, tell the guards to lead in Ludo."

It seemed as if a frost had penetrated the barn floor. Everything rustled, the eyes of all were turned towards the door, and there was some whispering.

Ludo came in. He looked over the gathering, but there was not enough light on the barn floor to permit him a view of all the legionnaires. Neither was there any time for it, as Father Imrich at once asked him to tell what he had to say.

Ludo's voice seemed to have broken. His face was emaciated and his eyes faint. One could see he was greatly fatigued. He tried to brace himself and speak loudly, but it wouldn't go.

"Forgive me, but I've gone through a lot for the past few days, about which Father Pavol and Father Imrich and Frater Ján already know. I am terribly fatigued; therefore, bear with me if it should be hard to utter some of the sentences."

At this he took out a small package from an inner pocket of his coat. He held it in his right hand and spoke silently, without accent, as though he were confessing or bringing a great message.

"I should have been at the funeral of a great man, an upright fighter, one of us, and in addition a relative of mine. But I was unable to attend. Communists martyred Dubovan, and at that time were at my heels; besides I also had other duties. I unable to attend the funeral, but here bring a handful of humus from his grave, which I visited the day after the funeral.

"I talked with his afflicted wife. In her great grief she told me: 'Tell relatives, friends, and all who knew my husband not to forget what he died for.'

"Here is the humus." At this, Ludo stepped up to Father Imrich and handed the package to him with the words: "Reverend Father, together with Frater Ján take custody of this ground and sprinkle some of it on every grave of our martyrs; take some of it to the graves of the great sons of our people. May they meet at least symbolically; and there, in the heavenly kingdom, may they obtain for us sufficient strength to follow their example."

"We will preserve Dubovan's memory in our hearts," solemnly spoke Father Imrich as he took over the humus from Ludo. "Dubovan was not an ordinary man. He is numbered among those who electrified the people and held it in opposition against Communism. And they so feared Dubovan that they destroyed him. But they have not killed Dubovan's honor, even as they failed to kill the honor of many others. Their example, their great sacrifice, and their martyrdom are our greatest encouragement.

"In Dubovan we've lost a great man, but gained a great patron in heaven. Let us here silently offer our prayers for him and then imitate his ways. Let every one of us be another Dubovan. Every village and every movement needs at least one Dubovan. Raise up your eyes to the heavens, brother legionnaires!"

Strong men knelt down and fixed their gaze upon the earth. The lamp seemed to wink its eyes, for a sad ceremony was about to take place.

"It has pleased your goodness, O God of the weak, to summon your faithful companion and to crown him with the wreath of martyrdom. May your name be praised, and may angels light his way in the courtyard of your heart, that he may see the end of his eternal journey in the peace of paradise. Grant him mercy and admit him to the ranks of your chosen ones. But give us sinful and imperfect men the strength to imitate our brother and do all for the honor of your name and the glory of our people, whom the brother that we remember and so pitifully pray for served so well that he sacrificed his noble life for it. May perpetual light shine on him forever! Amen."

The lamp was extinguished and darkness engulfed the fighters who had gathered here. Now they dispersed, each going about his duties. It was necessary for them even in heavy moments to stand in the service of a great ideal and to protect the defenseless.

In a narrowed circle, Ludo concluded the entire painful chapter of the last moments of Dubovan. And the White Legionnaires wrote down this incident into their chronicle.

Murdered

FRANTIŠEK DUBOVAN awaited even a third visit of the communist police. Every night he would retire to an uneasy bed. His wife Anna placed two shirts on his night stand, so that he might be able to take them along if they should come for him at night.

Every time the dog barked or the neighbor's gate grated, Dubovan would open his eyes and listen. He would glance towards the windows and the door, to see whether anything unusual was taking place.

What he anticipated came about. And during the night.

Three men appeared in the doorway. Armed with automatics and dressed in leather coats.

The countenance of the one was more brutal than the other, and the third looked like a patricide. The blinking flare of their flashlight made the three forms look even more ghostlike.

"Dubovan, are you home?" spoke up the harsh voice of a soldier.

"Yes, home. And who are you?"

"Ask no question! You will learn soon enough. Get up, and in five minutes we want you to be dressed. For the commissar is inquisitive about you."

Dubovan did not resist. He had decided a long time ago not to start anything with soldiers. Not that he was not conscious of his innocence, but because, besides his wife

201

Anna and himself, there was no one else at home. He had no arms and was already rather old. For just a month ago he had celebrated his seventieth birthday. So what could he gain by resistance?

But he did not fail to say his piece: "Couldn't you have come during daylight? I am not ashamed to go through the streets in the light of God's day. My conscience is clear. I have robbed no one, and there is no weight of any kind on my soul. I can look either a priest or civil authority squarely in the eye. You should have slept peacefully. You and the commissar. You could have come tomorrow; or you might have come yesterday to take me in. If you have no feeling for my old bones, here are both of my hands. Tie me up, for I may run away. By jove, I *will* run away! Are you not afraid?"

Only now did it dawn on one of the soldiers that this was ridicule, the answer of upright Dubovan. He cursed only as a criminal knows how to curse. "Do not resist, you bourgeois hog! We are not here to take instructions from you. We do our duty and want to fulfill it."

At this the three of them jumped Dubovan. One trained his automatic on him at close range, while the others tied his hands with a tight knot. One of them shoved him to go on.

"And not a sound out of you on the street, Dubovan. Otherwise we will shoot at once."

Dubovan remained silent. When they got out into the yard, Duncho started barking as if there were a company of soldiers on the march. The soldiers set out at double quick time and dragged Dubovan to make him step faster. Were they afraid? *Could* they be afraid? Did they know enough to be afraid?

Dubovan did not ask, but had these questions at the tip of his tongue. But why ask questions of monsters? Strange people with a questionable past and a mission from hell?

Dubovan remained silent, and it seemed to him that the soldiers were conscious of it.

They soon passed through the darkened street and went off to the side, so as to reach the market place quickly. There stood a building, the headquarters of the militia. Its windows were faintly lighted, a sign that someone was on service.

But there was more than that, for the commander was there. The commissar himself awaited Dubovan.

It seemed to him that he smiled when they shoved Dubovan into the door and announced that they had found him in bed.

Was it a smile, or was it the deceptive flash of light about the mouth of the commander of the militia? This question flashed through Dubovan's mind. But what of that? They did not give him a hearing. Neither were they curious about him. The commander ordered: "Take him out to solitary confinement!"

They led him out. It was dark there. They shoved him through the door, where he did not know. When they locked him up, he began feeling about. Wall, bare wall. One close to the other. He went around. His feet touched a hard bed. He felt on it a straw mattress with a thin quilt.

He hadn't slept well, but neither was he very tired. Nevertheless, he lay down on the bed.

He reflected. Not about the fact that they had brought him here, but how they had brought him. He had been prepared for this. He recalled how he had agreed with his wife and son not to make it bad for themselves. To him it no longer made any difference. For it was only yesterday that he had told Anna: "The light of my life is burning out. But you are younger. You are healthy and strong. You have a son, and his children need someone. If they should take me, and I do not return, do not allow yourselves to be broken down. Neither cast yourselves into anyone's arms. Live quietly and work that you may have something to eat, in order to preserve your faith and health. And the rest will take care of itself."

"Be careful and trust in God; no one will comfort me any more," added František Dubovan to himself aloud in the prison. And he knelt down beside the hard bed and said his night prayers half-aloud. He had said his prayers today for the second time. But this was the first time in prison.

They had already investigated him twice. And their statements had convinced Dubovan that they wanted to imprison him. In vain did he explain that he did not know the youth who had come to their homes; and that they had given him some money only to get rid of him.

Communists knew what they were doing. They wanted to punish Dubovan, because his brother had gone off to the West. And today he was in America.

Dubovan knew nothing, where his brother was or what he was doing. He only guessed; and someone had told him that his brother was in America. And if they told that to him, surely the communists also knew about it. And who knew whether the communists themselves had not broadcast this report?

Therefore Dubovan had been waiting. He had waited them out. Now he would continue to wait. But he did not bother his head about what would happen tomorrow or the day after. He had long ago decided how he would act. He had met several Slovaks who had been in prison during the communistic era, and had talked to their families. Therefore, he knew what their "justice" was like.

"At the least excuse, they will hold me facing a powerful light for hours. Maybe they will strip me naked and chop me about the most tender parts of the body with a rubber blackjack. And who knows whether they will not hang me on a pole by the hands and leave me there until I give them the signal that I will betray everything?"

So thought František Dubovan. And he would have continued thinking had sleep not overtaken him.

Guards awakened him in the morning. They knocked on the door, opened it, and gave him coffee. It was real coffee. And with it was decent black bread. A sizable piece. He quieted and warmed up his stomach. Dubovan wondered why they gave him such coffee and so much bread. They did not feast prisoners that way.

"Surely they don't want to win you over when they give you a hearing?" Dubovan asked himself when the last gulp of warm coffee slid down his throat.

They did not summon Dubovan for a hearing—neither the first nor the second day. They only took him out for a walk. A soldier accompanied him out into the yard. He went across the yard twice, then the soldier led him to the woodshed. He showed him a pile of cut wood and told him to stack it up.

Dubovan did his job. The overseer amused himself, scarcely taking notice of Dubovan.

"Do they want to find out whether I would idle and cheat them?" again he asked himself. But he could not answer.

"I know how to work. For I've worn myself out behind the plow for several years. Why wouldn't I stack up these sticks? At least it will while away the time. This really is a good diversion."

Dubovan stacked up the wood; then he got up and asked the overseer: "What now?"

"Come with me."

He led him back to solitary confinement. There books awaited him. Some kind of a story book, and beneath—he didn't want to believe it—the Bible! Beside the books was a thick candle.

Dubovan wondered what this meant. He looked over the Bible. He saw that it had been published during the administration of the Republic of Slovakia. He rubbed his eyes, doubtful whether this was really true or only a dream.

It *was* true. Dubovan had plenty to read, and he read to his heart's content. For he often had read the Bible aloud for his wife and son. And more than once, when he came home from church, he would repeat the sermon word for word.

Now it was pleasant for him to read the Bible in this solitary confinement. He was so engrossed in reading that he couldn't even afford to think of the reason why the communists had given him this precious treasure. He forgot entirely.

And so it seemed that the commissar also forgot about Dubovan. Only the inspector came around and brought him food. Good coffee and bread, and soup for dinner containing meat; for supper there was a glass of milk, and again bread, and sometimes soup. But altogether decent soup, with plenty of fat in it.

Dubovan fared well. He did not complain about the solitary confinement. He could read the Bible, and at night he had a candle. The thick candle lasted for three days. But they brought him a new one.

And when the second candle had burned halfway down, someone gently rapped on the door of Dubovan's cell. Such rapping usually occurs only on office doors and those of private dwellings.

And Dubovan answered, as he had been wont to do at home, "Come in."

In stepped the commissar.

"Are you satisfied, Dubovan?"

"Very much so," answered František.

"Have you enough to eat?"

"Sufficient."

"Do you need any other books for reading?"

"Thanks! But I'm not through with the Bible yet. And I have not even yet touched the story book—*The Unplowed Field*. This suffices for the time being."

"How do you sleep?"

"Well."

"In a word, you do not complain about the management of the prison?"

"I have no cause for it."

"I wanted to know, for a person can't always rely on inspectors. Even yesterday we released one of them for stealing bread and beating prisoners unmercifully. It all depends on you whether anything happens to you. You get only what you deserve."

He turned and left.

"As I *deserve*? It is true that they do not treat me badly, but I don't deserve even that. For this bed is hard, the room dark and uncomfortable, and I have to answer Nature's calls in a corner. But it's not so bad, at that."

Such were Dubovan's first thoughts when the commissar left; but the train of ideas spun on: "Why do they treat me so?" He did not philosophize much about it, but ended farmer-fashion: "While they are catching the bird, they sing sweetly for him. Watch out, Dubovan, lest they catch and strangle you! This is but a trap. They will strike."

The days of decent food, walks, work in the woodshed, and nightly reading of the Bible and the story book continued. The guards also brought him other books. All nice reading. Instructive and entertaining.

Dubovan gulped it all down. He thought that he should read through everything, for who knows whether there would be time for it on the morrow or the day after? He cared for little else, only kept on reading. He reconciled himself with life and wanted to make full use of these fine moments afforded to him by the . . . communists.

But, nevertheless, here and there he wondered why they were doing this. He had no answer. And he thought that the devil himself was tempting him.

Finally, however, he learned all. The commissar came. Dubovan repeated just how he felt and saw things.

But the commissar had also a new question: "Is it true that you have a brother in America?"

"Maybe he is there."

"What kind of *maybe?* Can't you answer a question directly?" asked the commissar as he raised his voice.

"No, for there is only talk that my brother has gone to America. I have no report about it."

"Are you not in touch with him? Does he not write to you?"

"No."

"And what about that visit from Germany? Why, that was his messenger!"

"I do not believe it. And he sent nothing. That person came but to spy on me."

"We know all, Dubovan. You can deny nothing. Your brother is in America. It concerns us very much that you write him a letter."

"How can I write to him when I don't know the address?"

"You *do* know it! You make excuses, as does every affected pious fellow, hypocrite, and enemy of the socialistic order."

Dubovan began to realize that not everything was in order.

But he could not gather his wits. The commissar would not allow him to. He insisted: "Will you write it?"

Dubovan became silent.

The commissar seemingly wanted to work on a chance: "We want nothing special from you; only write your brother that you have it good, that in this prison we treat prisoners very well, give them good food, and bring them instructive reading according to their taste. In a word, that you have nothing to complain about—as you yourself stated twice, and I also noted on paper."

The commissar said this very softly, and even more softly continued: "In America they have strong antisocialistic propaganda. Capitalists attack us peace-loving people and make up all kinds of tales about us. One such tale is that we torture people in prison and finally even kill them. You have been here for two weeks and have experienced what life in these prisons of ours is like. I want nothing more than that you should emphasize that all who broadcast reports in America that we abuse prisoners—especially political prisoners—are making a mistake. Do this for me, Dubovan. Do this for our Communist Party, for the sake of peace which we uphold! We want American people to know only what is true about us."

"I will not do it, Mr. Commissar!"

"Disobedience is punished by officials, Dubovan."

At this the commissar used his hard fist, lunged and struck Dubovan in the chest. Dubovan fell to the ground, his voice losing itself in his throat. Only the words, "My God!" were spoken distinctly.

"All of you village rich are that way! As long as we feed you and keep the Pope before your nose, you are content. But when we want some service, you oppose us. You betray even your own mother!"

Again he lunged with his fist. But he restrained himself. Maybe he thought it over. He turned to the wall. For a while he considered; then, in a more moderate tone, he began talking to Dubovan. He thought of everything possible to get Dubovan to promise to write to America that everything was good in communist prisons.

But Dubovan did not promise. For the greater part, he did not even answer the commissar. He was convinced of what he wanted now. The commissar, too, realized that he was dealing with a tough Slovak farmer. Finally, he lost his self-control, ceased playing up to him; and when he had exhausted all his efforts, he threw himself upon old Dubovan. He bloodied his face. In addition, he kicked him in the stomach.

Dubovan rolled over on the ground. He fainted, and blood streamed down his face.

That day Dubovan got neither dinner nor supper. They but poured cold water over him to revive him. When he again refused to promise that he would write a letter to America, the new inspector placed pencils between the fingers of both his hands and then squeezed them as hard as he could, so that they were breaking. Dubovan wailed painfully, cried, and again rolled to the ground.

They left him alone all night. But Dubovan did not know it was night. For he slept hard. He had fainted. Strong pounding on the door awakened him around six in the morning.

Dubovan's head was heavy, his hands painful. The fingers were broken, so that he could not feel them. Everything ached. When he moved his hand over the floor, he felt an unpleasant, sticky dampness. It was his own blood, half-congealed. Its odor was unpleasant as it struck his nostrils. It is a test of nerves, to feel your own blood.

Dubovan was unable even to answer, and the inspector pounded the third time. Then he opened the door and roared at Dubovan: "Get up, you dumb farm dog! The commissar is waiting for you."

This had no effect on Dubovan. They had beaten him to a bloody pulp; they tortured him. He was unable either to stand or to give an answer. He but whispered: "I am unable to."

The inspector stepped up to Dubovan, bent over him,

grabbed him by the right arm, and tried to stand him on his feet. But this wouldn't do. He kicked him in the foot, cursed, and then, picking Dubovan up in his arms, he walked off with him, as the commissar had ordered. He set him down in the commissar's office.

The commissar roared, "When did you have it any better, Dubovan? Why, we even carry you around in our arms like a baby."

But Dubovan did not wink even an eyelash.

The commissar placed many questions. But the louder he shouted, and the more he vented his anger, the less hope he had for an answer. He ordered the inspector to teach old Dubovan some order. The inspector beat him with a blackjack over the head, the back, the stomach, and over the most tender parts of the body.

Dubovan was no longer a man. He was but a pile of human misery. Humped into a ball, he would give evidence of life here and there when a vein would move or a nerve jump. And that was all.

The commissar roared. He got a weak answer—only the echo from the dumb walls of the bloody prison.

The old man Dubovan did not hold out. That very day his soul left his body.

The Penitent

THE WHITE LEGIONNAIRES called a council of elders to discuss Ludo's case, for Father Pavol had recommended him for Legion membership. They looked through his past activities. They were satisfied with him on all but one count: It wasn't clear to them why he had become involved with Cyril. They therefore delegated Father Imrich to clear up this point.

Ludo openly told Father Imrich that he had considered Cyril an underground worker against communism. But when Dubovan had cautioned him about Cyril's suspicious behavior, he had watched his step. He did not renounce him, but tried to get all the information he could out of him. But when he caused Dubovan to be imprisoned, he showed up very infrequently, even though Ludo had promised that they would also go after Father Pavol. Finally, he came around and they made an agreement. Cyril promised a reward, and this was all the more suspicious to Ludo. At last they agreed as to the day.

"In the meantime, the sad report that Dubovan had died in prison came out. I wanted to put off the journey to Father Pavol; but I decided to keep the original appointment, so that Father Pavol would not let up on his vigilance and I might not become an object of suspicion to Cyril and his superiors."

"And what did you do?" asked Father Imrich.

"As I have already told you, I did not go to Uncle Dubovan's funeral; for on the third day I was to be at Father Pavol's. And I also had other matters to attend to at Bratislava. But as I had agreed with Cyril, even so we met at the rectory in Huta. Exactly on the hour.

"Father Pavol greeted Cyril very decently. At the start Cyril seemed to be heedless, in a way trying to make it appear as though he were fleeing from communists and seeking refuge at the rectory, for he said that he had heard a lot of good about it and its manager. That everyone found refuge, help and protection there."

"So Father Pavol had a good guest," spoke Imrich.

"I had prepared him for it, and he knew that Cyril might be an agent. Therefore, he tried to draw out all he could from him. Father Pavol gave him some questions he could not answer. For example: 'You say that you have good connections with anticommunist workers at the highest places in Bratislava. Could you give me at least one of their names?'

"Cyril cast down his eyes, as though he were thinking—and this was a bad sign. After a while he said: 'Milan Vrbina.'

" 'I think that you are either mistaken, or Vrbina is deceiving you, for he is a confidant of the communists.'

"Cyril wanted to cover up and said: 'Why, he was the one who gave me your name!'

211

" 'Many have already made use of my name!' was the answer Cyril got from Father Pavol. 'That is no sign that Mr. Vrbina is in the service of the underground. Cyril, I warn you against such people! You would be missed. You are needed in the service of the people. But as long as we are at it, you visited my relative Dubovan and asked him to give you money for his brother. Did you forward that money to its destination?'

" 'Yes.'

" 'Did you give it to Dubovan's brother?'

" 'Not to him, but to his trusted man, Urban.'

" 'Where?'

" 'In Vienna.'

" 'And do you know that Urban is in Slovakia?'

" 'He mentioned that he would come here and work as a confidant of Dubovan.'

" 'He also deceived you. For Urban is imprisoned for communistic extortion.'

" 'By whom was he imprisoned?'

" 'By righteous anticommunistic workers.'

"Cyril was bewildered and could not at once resume conversation. Father Pavol helped him again. 'Were you ever imprisoned, Cyril?'

" 'To what period do you refer, Father Pavol?'

" 'In general, were you ever imprisoned? For example, at present, as a general rule, communists imprison anyone who seeks encounters. And it seems to me that you do seek them. Once you are in Munich, then in Vienna, you go freely after Dubovan, and now you are here to see me at the rectory. And with all this, you claim to play an important role in the service of the anticommunistic underground. I think you are extremely lucky that they have not caught up with you thus far. I do not deny that I have been imprisoned twice already, and they wanted to drag me away even a third time. What have you to say for yourself?'

" 'I was not imprisoned,' said Cyril, somehow forcing himself to calmness.

"But here he tripped himself. Both Father Pavol and I

212

knew that at their second visit to Dubovan the soldiers had specifically mentioned the spy Cyril. At that time a soldier had jumped Dubovan with the question: " 'Was there a certain Cyril visiting you?'

" 'He was.'

" 'And what did he want?'

" 'He tempted me, even as did other of his kind.'

" 'And did he not ask you for money?'

" 'That I do not even remember.'

" 'Read this.' And the soldier handed Uncle Dubovan a 'notebook' containing Cyril's own handwriting, in which he assured the management of the Bratislava police that he had accepted money from Dubovan, to be used for the treacherous activity of his brother in western Europe.

"After that Dubovan no longer denied, but admitted everything. But he also added that he had given Cyril the money mostly to get rid of him, for he was an unpleasant guest. 'And we know all this, Cyril,' said Father Pavol.

" 'I think that the soldiers were deceiving, even as they deceive in many such cases.'

" 'Maybe,' said Father Pavol in an even tone. 'But you will never get me where you got Dubovan.'

"At this the door opened and two powerful men appeared.

" 'Take this man under your supervision,' said Father Pavol. 'But do not harm him. Just place him in safe custody, that he may not escape. And search him thoroughly.'

"They searched him," continued Ludo. "And they found on him a notebook. It contained all kinds of names—but they could not make out much of it. It was all quite garbled. He had had a good education. Father Pavol visited him twice and had long talks with him. At first, he was venomous. He was so overpowered with anger that he literally raved.

" 'That was a sign that he was not one of us,' Father Pavol told me.

"And he certainly was *not* one of us! Father Pavol wants to bring him here. If you and the council of elders agree, give Cyril a public hearing. This would also help me out."

Father Imrich, together with the guards, set out secretly

for Huta. On the next day he gave the recommendation to the council of elders that Ludo be accepted as a regular member of the Legion, and that Cyril be called up before the board. The council of elders agreed and nominated Ludo for membership.

Three days later, the meeting was held at Philip's hillside. At the recommendation of the council of elders, Ludo was accepted without preliminaries, even though one of the members first asked why Ludo sent a letter by Cyril to Dubovan.

"He sent that letter only because he thought it was the right thing to do. This was the first opportunity he had ever had to join in anticommunistic activity, so he did it. But he made up for it, for he saved Father Pavol and caught Cyril." This was Father Imrich's explanation.

"In that case, I make a motion that he be accepted unanimously," said the Legionnaire who had made the exception.

"As I have said," took over Father Imrich after Ludo had taken the obligatory promise, "our newest member has caught Cyril, a dangerous spy and a murderer of Dubovan. Today we are assembled here to meet Cyril and to hear him, if he decides to talk. Afterwards you should decide what should be done with him. Father Pavol makes the motion, and I second it, that we maintain our traditional discipline here, as well as our Christian charity. We are not as heedless as the communists. We do not provoke scandals, give no cause for bloodshed, and shun all violence. Therefore, I am for it, especially as Cyril is still a young man, one who became a communist more from the spirit of adventure than of conviction. We must not harm him needlessly. We will do all we can to bring him back to the right path; and if it is necessary, and you agree on it, we will keep him segregated in our hideouts. We priests will take him under our direction so that we may bring him back to the society of good people. Do you agree?"

"That is very good," resounded a voice from the barn floor; and immediately all cried out: "Let it be so!"

"I ask you, then, that we decide who will question Cyril

when the guards bring him in. I would nominate Brother Jozef."

"Right, let it be Brother Jozef!"

"Matúš, give the guards the sign to bring Cyril in."

Once again the barn floor rustled. This was the first time they would question a murderer of one of their toughest fighters. Jozef's gaze was lost among the rafters. He was probably praying, considering how he should fulfill his task. He did not move an eyelash as he waited for what was to happen. They heard footsteps out in the yard, then some shouting, but it soon subsided.

The doors were opened, and Cyril was pushed in by two guards.

"Take off his chains," said Father Imrich.

Cyril timidly raised his head. His green eyes glistened, even as they did on that morning when he had aroused Ludo in Bratislava. A cold chill went over Ludo, and even though the thought of Uncle Dubovan made it hard for him, still, he pitied Cyril at that moment.

"Brethren," spoke Father Imrich, "you have decided. Cyril, who, for his youthful years, has done a lot of evil, is here. Jozef, take the chair."

"Step forward, Cyril," spoke the tall Legionnaire.

He stepped closer, standing almost underneath the lamp, so that the rays of light fell on his face. The Legionnaires looked at Cyril and Jozef, and some of them on Ludo and Father Imrich. The guards returned to the door.

"Is it true what we have found about you—that you betrayed Dubovan and that you were also about to talk Father Pavol into a venture equally as dangerous as Dubovan's?"

Cyril remained silent. He bowed his head, while his eyes zigzagged over the Legionnaires sitting on the straw.

"Answer, Cyril!" said Jozef. "If you do not answer today, we have time for it tomorrow. But answer, you will."

"You ask too much of me," Cyril finally ventured to say.

"And was the death of a human being anything less?"

"Do not burden me with the responsibility for Dubovan's death," continued Cyril. "The soldiers and the whole Party knew of Dubovaň. If I had not gone after him, they would have sent someone else."

"Therefore, you do admit it. That is enough for us. We are not concerned about whether they would have sent someone else, but with the fact that *you* went and fulfilled *your* inhuman mission! You have murdered a human being."

"I did not kill him! Those are cutting words!"

"Moreover, you aimed at still another—and that a priest!"

"I did not intend it. I already wanted to escape."

"You say that now, but your plans were entirely different. You wanted to get the great reward offered for Father Pavol. You wanted to get ahead of the soldiers, who had not been able to drag Father Pavol away. You wanted to become an expert in catching good people—our leaders! This is not such a simple matter, Cyril."

Cyril nervously looked towards the door. At this one of the Legionnaires got up and placed himself close behind him.

"There's no sense in denying and twisting things about, Cyril," continued Jozef. "We know about it all. Thus far, nothing has happened to you, and you know well that we could have revenged ourselves on you already in Huta, if revenge had been our motive. We know that you have perpetrated a terrible act. You have sinned against heaven and human justice. The blood of an innocent man is on your hands. The money which you have taken from him, and maybe others, will burn you. Every false word that you have uttered will be a sword prodding your conscience. We will not permit you again to murder, betray and deceive upright people in towns and villages."

"Do not harm me! I am innocent," cried Cyril, and he jerked his entire frame as if he wanted to emphasize that he was really innocent.

"Awhile ago you said something entirely different. You are guilty of plots and snares against Dubovan. You carry the guilt of his death. Brethren, I think it will be good if the council of elders holds a consultation and brings out a verdict on that admission. If Cyril denies the second point of

216

the accusation, we will not waste time. For we will find out about it also. What do you think about it? Make a motion."

Before a motion could be made, Cyril spoke: "If you want to pass judgment, judge everything at once. Father Pavol was to meet the same fate that overtook Dubovan. I was supposed to talk him into meeting a strong 'anticommunist' group in Nové Zámky. There they would have caught him."

"Have they taught you that, Cyril? Do you want to make a cheap confession, and then escape from us? If such are your plans, you are mistaken," said Jozef.

"Tell openly how it happened," interposed Father Imrich.

"I have told all. Do you want still more? You told me to admit it."

"This concerns not only admission, but also the circumstances. That we may know *why* you did it, and whether you still stubbornly persist in your errors. We are not interested in taking it out on you; we do not want to wrong you."

Cyril maintained a dead silence and looked at the ground. It seemed that he would do no more talking. Or was it really so?

Cyril was undergoing an internal struggle. His sensitivity was awakened. The nerves of his right temple twitched, and his face reddened. Blood rushed to his face and hands. He felt something in his veins, as though he were dreaming, or as if a new man were being born.

"So it is, Cyril," whispered his conscience, "you are young. You still have time enough to live as a decent person. This seems to be an opportune moment to break with a wicked world, to admit even ugly facts, to admit sincerely what you have done. And *do* it—even as they ask you to! These people will not harm you. If they punish you, bear it manfully. For nothing good awaits you, even if you should leave this place with your hide intact. Communists will not trust you. They have kicked aside many of their paid agents once they have fallen into the hands of the enemy. Communists believe you only as long as you are under their supervision. Once they lose sight of you, even though it be by accident, they will not trust you, for they fear you. And

217

they fear those most who thoroughly understand them."

So thought Cyril. He did not raise his head. He was either unable to, or did not want to, in order to concentrate on new thought. He considered the circumstances, and resolved to tell all and repent. "For, even if I should be mistaken in these people, they will not be worse than the communists. Therefore, let it happen as it will."

After a while he said: "I confess all. I have sinned against the law of God and against Dubovan, against Father Pavol and the whole nation. I resign myself to you, so that I may once more be able to face my mother entirely cleansed. Do as you see fit."

"We are not judges of our own cause, Cyril. We are people whom the communists have chased into the hills. We are not murderers. We will not defile our hands—even with your blood," said Jozef. "But the sense of justice bids us to inform you that for so great a crime you will not be able to breathe God's free air for a certain length of time. Therefore, brethren, I again make the motion that the council of elders depart for a consultation. Does Cyril want to say anything more?"

Cyril raised his head and looked sharply into Jozef's eyes. "If I may, I'd like you to hear me before you leave for the consultation. I am young. I probably acted in haste. But I've done a terrible thing. I admit it. I have before my eyes the picture of my mother, who cautioned me to keep away from communists. I did not obey her. Wild dreams goaded me on. They were more to me than my mother. But for the sake of my mother, and because I once learned that it's never too late to return if one repents, I beg—beg all of you, to hear me. I do not want to bribe my way out. I am willing to suffer for what I've done. If you think that I am unworthy to remain in decent society, act according to your laws. I see that you do not torture people. I had met prisoners of yours, and they looked good. There were no signs of beatings on them. They did not complain. On the contrary, they said there was a great difference between the communist police and you. In fact, there was no comparison.

"Again I say that I do not want to save myself; I do not want a mitigation of punishment, for I see that you are just. And you have reason to be severe when they murder your good fighters. But I would like to tell you, if you will hear me first before you decide and lead me away, that you may all know what I've experienced and what is being prepared for you."

"Are you for it, brethren, that Cyril should tell of his experiences?" asked Jozef.

A muscled Legionnaire got up and raised his hand. Jozef gave him the floor.

"Let him speak—but only truth; and do not allow him to gain time with tales. We know that communists are even now tracking us down. But let him have his say. Thus, we will be better able to judge his intentions."

"Has anyone any other idea?" asked Jozef.

No one spoke up.

"Are you for it that Cyril speak?"

"Yes," answered almost all of them.

"You may have the floor, Cyril."

Cyril straightened out, coughed, and slowly began. "In the first place, I would want to say that communists are doing everything possible against the underground movement; that they get all its leaders as soon as possible. You do know about that. But maybe you do not know that they are trying to implant their own people into every cell. They even organize so-called 'anticommunist' bands themselves, in order to entice people into them, and thus liquidate them as soon as possible.

"Communists will not let up in this work till they have broken down opposition entirely—or a revolution forces them to leave Slovakia and the rest of the countries.

"Communist police use young people, especially, for their service. They do this artfully, in order to break down character and quickly educate for themselves trusted servants. Money, women and liquor help; and weaker ones are taken in. I know this from practical experience. I myself was disgusted with it more than once, as they offered me all kinds of comforts, until at times they made me sick.

"The police department is under the control of the most morally depraved people, non-Slovaks mostly, occupying responsible positions. They perpetrate all kinds of atrocities. Any one of you who has ever been at police headquarters, or otherwise imprisoned, is acquainted with this fact. But those whom they have killed cannot talk. Such testimony can be given only by those who will reform and have the courage to admit how wrong they have been.

"I have the courage to tell of them. And I will relate them in order—what I have heard, seen and experienced.

"I testify how I once heard two soldiers talking—boasting— how they had helped in the overthrow of Slovakia in 1944. This was the word-for-word utterance of one of them: 'Nothing would have succeeded without the Soviets. And had it not been for Beneš' pro-Soviet foreign government, who knows whether that Slovak rectory government would not have pulled through it all without a scratch?'

"And then they broke out into diabolical laughter over an incident of two murdered priests. One of them said: 'I do not know whether you have heard about the rectors, Salát and Seda?'

" 'I have not,' answered his comrade.

" 'Anton Salát was one of the most furious enemies of Communism. He lectured and wrote against the proletariat. Consequently, our men caught him early in the first week of the 'uprising' at the rectory of Hájniky, and led him to the bridge on the River Hron. Salát begged permission at least to go to confession. But nothing of the kind was allowed him. They shot him, took his gold watch and gold teeth, and cast the body into the Hron. And Seda in Liptov got even more. They cut belts of hide from his back while he was still alive, cut out his privates, and thus left him to die a slow death.'

"These and similar events I heard in Bratislava. Maybe they also wanted to frighten me. Once it was related how, somewhere near Banská Bystrica, near Handlová and near

Zilina, they shot down people over open graves which the victims themselves had to dig out.

"And I was shocked also by other matters. In 1944, the communists were prepared for everything, even capture. And when they would fall into the hands of Germans, they would enter their service, then go about towns and villages in German uniforms, picking out and shooting down the best anticommunist workers, whom they had marked out a long time ago. Or some foreigners who had remained in Slovakia during the period of its independence would simultaneously serve two sides—the government and the communists; and when the overthrow of 1944 came about, they betrayed to Germans such people as the communists wanted liquidated. It was in this way that many Slovaks, whom German soldiers had dragged away at the outbreak of the overthrow got into Germany; they recrossed the frontiers of Slovakia in the fall of 1944, so as not to be forced to fight against Soviet parachutists and the international communistic partisan brigades being formed in the hills of Slovakia.

"I have heard about a certain burgess—I can no longer recall his name—he was from Turiec—whom they tied to a wagon sometime in the summer of 1945. They then harnessed a team of horses to the wagon and dragged the burgess behind the wagon for a distance of some ten kilometers until he died.

"Already in 1945, commissars boasted about how many typewriters they had stolen from bishops' offices, and what they robbed from cloisters and rectories they had devastated.

"I was in Bratislava during the court action against the three Catholic bishops. The commissar laughed uproariously when he related how the supposedly senile bishop, Ján Vojtaššák, had prattled, and how everything had succeeded for them. He added: 'And the same also awaits the rest of them. It is but a matter of time. For the present this suffices. Three of them got their medicine; the rest will remain quiet for a while.'

"I've read the instructions on how to deal with farmers.

221

They were to promise them steady employment at the collective centers, with the same benefits that other workers get for working for the communistic state. In towns where there was great opposition, they were to conduct petition-signing ventures for collective centers. And if this did not help, the poorest farmers were to be incited to rebellion against the village rich, thus creating the impression that the village 'desired' unity of association.

"The army and every other organization in contact with the public were infiltrated with confidants and spies. These, in turn, handed in reports to the Party and the secret police, and everything was conducted accordingly. They had such confidants also in bishops' offices. The bishop could not make a single step without them. They listened in on his conversation over the telephone and noted every visitor. Agents also attended, and still attend, every church service, where they listen to every word of the priest and note down all those who attend church regularly.

"Thus, for example, one such agent told us in class how he was to follow a certain man who worked in the same establishment. This man was a member of the Communist Party; in spite of this, however, he attended church services. At a competitive council meeting, that agent told him: 'Since you are a church member, comrade, do not hide behind the fourth pillar to the left, for God does not see you there.'

"And then he boasted how all laughed when he thus uncovered the man whom they had placed under his supervision.

"Thus it went on, and still goes on, case after case. The communists are organized. They have severe discipline. And when Prague does not suffice to supply them, help comes from Moscow. I have met many of these Russians.

"Murders and deportations, whether to Siberia, the uranium mines, or to the properties of expelled Sudeten Germans—these are all in the plans to weaken the nation and bend its backbone.

"Take the case of President Jozef Tiso. After the execution of the 'verdict,' a lot of drinking took place at the police headquarters of Bratislava. And all those present were possessed with satanic laughter over how they had removed their number-one enemy in Slovakia.

" 'And those followers of the Pope should have tried something,' cried the commissar. 'We had the army and the police ready for them.'

"This much is certain—they hanged Tiso because he was the most stubborn enemy of Communism. And the fact that he was opposed to any and all forms of Czecho-Slovakia was of secondary importance, because Slovak Communist leaders themselves wanted an independent Soviet Slovak Republic.

"I conclude my talk. I have told what I know. If it should interest you, I can tell even more. Finally, I would want to remind you of one thing: I have not spoken here in my own behalf. You have me in your power. Do as you will with me. Act according to the principles of justice. But upon my honor, I want to proclaim that I have recognized the errors of my ways; and it will depend upon you whether I will be worthy once more to go to my family home and look the mother, who had always warned me against Communism, squarely in the eye."

Cyril ceased talking. He cast down his eyes and waited. . . .

"Brethren, you have heard Cyril's talk. What is your wish?" asked Jozef.

"Let the council of elders consult and decide on the basis of this hearing and admission."

"Is there any other motion?" asked Jozef.

A silence of the grave was his answer. Finally, two cried out at once: "We entrust the entire case to the council of elders."

The council of elders departed at once for the consultation. Father Imrich stepped up to Cyril and pressed his hand. Frater Ján did likewise, and told him: "I am a relative of the murdered Dubovan. But I know that he too would forgive you if he could speak to us here from heaven. Therefore, I, too, forgive you."

"And I, Cyril," spoke up Ludo.

Some others also joined in and assented; others asked Cyril

questions. They were curious concerning details about the people and events Cyril had mentioned a short time ago. He answered gravely, and it seemed that his spiritual peace was returning. A light burned in his eyes. Maybe it was a fire of uncertainty, a little fear, or the joy over his return to decent company. Cyril was changing. In his thoughts he was returning to his mother, and was overjoyed that he was able to free himself from those monstrous red spiders.

"I am prepared even for great penances," he said, as the door opened and all the members of the council of elders, with Jozef at their head, marched in.

Jozef stepped up on the elevation and waited until all the members of the council had taken their places. He asked the brother Legionnaires to arise.

"Seeking justice and adhering to Christian principles, and also mindful of Cyril's youthful age, the council of elders has decided to sentence Cyril to six years of imprisonment and a year of probation in restricted territory. I present this motion of the council of elders for consideration, and ask for your decision."

"Agreed! We agree! It is proper," sounded a voice.

Cyril was led away, and his countenance reflected satisfaction.

Out in the yard the guards leading Cyril away met messengers who brought in the following report: "We have friends on the neighboring hillside who yesterday stopped a freight train hauling thirty carloads of Slovak sugar to Soviet Russia. Our men were prepared and attacked the train, taking in great booty. The entire complement of the train, together with ten armed soldiers—who were enjoying themselves playing cards in one of the cars—was taken. They also obtained a great quantity of sugar. We will have enough of it for all our local groups to last several years."

"Slovakia is at attention. We guard what is our own and will not allow ourselves to be robbed. We will *not* give up," said Jozef.

And so he concluded the meeting so that the White Legionnaires might be able to continue in the work that the nation expected of them, a work which is part of the entire movement against Communism in central Europe. Lightning flashed over nearby hills, and Legionnaires hopefully awaited the thunder which would expel from Slovakia communistic intruders and foreign rulers. But they did not wait with folded hands.

Even as any other great people, they wanted to earn their freedom!

About the Author

Joseph Paučo, son of a Slovak farmer, was born in 1914, and educated at the Slovak University in Bratislava, where he received his Ph.D. in 1942. A journalist by profession, he worked with the influential daily *"Slovák"* from 1938 to 1945, serving as editor-in-chief from 1942 to 1945. In 1945 he fled with his wife to Austria; then to West Germany; and finally made his way to New York City in 1950.

Intensely active in the Slovak liberation movement, Dr. Paučo has served since 1950 as assistant editor of the weekly *Jednota*, most widely distributed American-Slovak newspaper. He is secretary-general of the Slovak National Council Abroad, most representative organization of Slovak exiles in the Free World; a member of the American Academy of Political and Social Science, Philadelphia; of the Slovak Writers and Artists Association, Cleveland, Ohio; and is associated with the Institute of Ethnic Studies at Georgetown University. In 1958, for his anti-Communist activities here and in his native land, he was sentenced to death by the Soviet regime in Bratislava.

Dr. Paučo, whose home is in Middletown, Pennsylvania, is author of seven books, numerous studies, and more than 900 articles in Slovak, and has been widely published in Slovakia and in this country.